WILD
PENINSULA

LAURA NELSON BAKER

WILD
PENINSULA

drawings by Earl Thollander

The Story of
Point Reyes National Seashore

with an introduction
by Stewart L. Udall

ATHENEUM   1969   NEW YORK

to my sister
ALMA NELSON STENSRUD
one of the kindest persons I know

ACKNOWLEDGMENTS

MANY PERSONS had a part in helping me gather material for this book, too many to be named. Special appreciation, however, should go to Robert H. Becker, Assistant Director of Bancroft Historical Library, University of California at Berkeley; Mrs. Katharine Miller Johnson, Washington, D.C.; Mr. William J. Duddleson of the Conservation Foundation, Washington, D.C.; Mrs. Jean Day, San Rafael Independent Journal librarian, San Rafael, Calif.; Supervisor Thomas T. Storer, Marin County, Calif.; the late Mrs. Caroline B. Livermore, San Francisco, Calif.; Mrs. Virginia Keating, Marin County Free Library director; Mrs. Diana MacArthur, National Conference on Natural Beauty and Conservation, New York, N.Y.; the Marin County Historical Society, and the staff of the Point Reyes National Seashore.

LAURA NELSON BAKER

INTRODUCTION

SOMEDAY YOU WILL go to Point Reyes. You will drive across the high, orange arch of San Francisco's Bay Bridge. You will quickly pass the suburbs of Marin County, ride up and down bare hills, see the sculptured earth of coastal California. The road will dip in and out of dark forests, fragrant with bay trees, and pass again into sunlight. At last you will be on a huge peninsula of magnificent vistas. The peninsula is Point Reyes, and Point Reyes is a National Seashore.

What does it mean to be a National Seashore? It means that Point Reyes is held in trust by the Federal government for all people, for all time. It belongs to you and me. It will belong to my grandchildren and yours too, someday.

National Parks and National Seashores don't just happen. They are established by Act of Congress, and Congress acts only when people demand.

It takes people who love the land and are willing to spend part of their lives to assure its preservation. It takes politicians who have a high sense of public interest. It takes many, many volunteer citizens who will spend their afternoons licking envelopes, and their evenings testifying at hearings, who will study the techniques of preservation, and persuade others to join their cause.

In the period between 1962 and 1968 conservationists supported Congress in the establishment of eight new National Seashores. Cape Cod was the first in 1962. Point Reyes was established in 1966, Fire Island in 1964, Cape Lookout in 1966. Additionally in 1968 Congress established a nationwide system of Scenic Rivers, and a nationwide system of Trails. It also achieved two new National Parks, Redwoods and North Cascades. These designations are one of the greatest conservation achievements of all time.

In addition to these great national treasures, it is equally valuable to have many, many state parks and local parks and trails near where you live.

What is it like near your home? Are meadows being bulldozed for shopping centers? Are you separated from the woods by lanes of freeway traffic? Do the woods have "keep out" signs?

If there is a nice natural area that you and your neighbors enjoy, there are many things you can do to save it. You can find out if it is on the State Outdoor Recreation Plan (Every state has such a plan). If it isn't, and you think it should be, you can do something about it. You can write to your Governor and legislators. You can write the President, and Cabinet members and Congressmen. Public officials welcome mail and will be guided by it. They care, particularly if you care.

You can join a conservation group like the Sierra Club, or the Audubon Society, or the Izaak Walton League, or a local conservation club. You can testify at public hearings. Some Boy Scouts did at the Point Reyes hearings, and they were listened to. America wants to hear the voice of youth.

One of the themes repeated throughout American history is how men have been challenged, and ennobled, and enriched by the land. In our own times we have developed the conservation tools to assure that this refreshing contact will continue. In the pages of Laura Nelson Baker's book, you will read about people who shaped the future of Point Reyes; people who themselves were molded by this great dramatic landscape that fronts the everlasting Pacific.

STEWART L. UDALL
FORMER SECRETARY
OF THE INTERIOR

CONTENTS

Acknowledgements   vii

Introduction by Stewart L. Udall   ix

Author's Note   xv

A GALLEON FINDS A HARBOR   3

INDIAN WELCOME   13

AN OPEN BOAT   29

THE MIWOK AND THE MISSION   40

WILD HORSE ROUNDUP   49

THE RED ELK GO
AND THE LIGHTHOUSE COMES   57

WHEN THE EARTH CRACKED   66

THE PLATE OF BRASSE   76

BATTLE FOR THE SEASHORE   85

AS A NATIONAL SEASHORE   100

Notes   115

AUTHOR'S NOTE

THE POINT REYES PENINSULA on the West Coast of the United States is a hundred square mile piece of land jutting into the Pacific Ocean about fifty miles north of the city of San Francisco, California, in the county of Marin. The road to the peninsula crosses the Golden Gate Bridge and runs along the coastal freeway, 101, until it breaks away near Greenbrae and goes west and north. This road is called Sir Francis Drake Boulevard. It travels through a number of small towns until it reaches Inverness, which is the entrance to the Point Reyes National Seashore park.

For hundreds of years the peninsula was occupied only by Miwok Indians. Around 1815, however, the Spanish priests came north from Mexico and built a mission near the Indian villages. The priests persuaded the Indians to leave their villages and join the mission settlement to learn white men's ways and often to contract white men's diseases. In a few years, most of the Miwok had disappeared or died.

After California became part of the United States in 1848, the beautiful coastline and the flourishing grasslands of Point Reyes peninsula were purchased for use as ranches and dairy farms. But dairying on a small scale began to be impractical in the late nineteen fifties and early nineteen sixties. Some of the ranchers sold their holdings to real estate developers for housing tracts and commercial sites. The conservationists became alarmed. They saw this rare unspoiled coast being lost forever to the people of the United States as a recreational resource. Interested citizens from all over the country persuaded the United States Congress to acquire Point Reyes peninsula for a national park. In September, 1962, 53,000 acres of the peninsula were set aside for acquisition by the federal government and a few years later the park service started to develop trails and roads and beaches. Over three hundred and fifty years from the time the first white man set foot on peninsula soil, the Point Reyes National Seashore took its place with other such seashore parks as a place for Americans to enjoy.

WILD
PENINSULA

A GALLEON
FINDS A HARBOR

THE FACES OF THE SAILORS working the ship's pump were dark with anger under their wet, soiled caps and they muttered together as they worked. Overhead, high up in the crow's nest, two of their comrades peered ahead of the *San Agustín* against the oncoming darkness, looking for a harbor. And on the poop deck of the Manila galleon, the ship's master, Sebastian Cermeño, studied the Pacific Ocean's eastern shore. From time to time he glimpsed smoke arising and once he saw the flame of a campfire. No beast, either of sea or forest, knew how to make fire. Cermeño realized that there must be human beings living on this wild, North Pacific coast.

"Ahoy, below!" called out one of the lookouts.

"Ahoy!" replied the captain, turning from the ship's rail and glancing upward. "What do you see?" Cermeño hoped the answer would not be "An English ship." His little sailing vessel was in no shape to give battle. But he would put up a fight if any marauder decided to attack. He was not going to be deprived of his rich cargo of silks and rare china.

The wind was rising and the sails began to fill. Cermeño ordered one of the lookouts to come down to the deck and report his sightings. When the man dropped off the rigging and made his way to where the captain stood, Cermeño studied his face and bearing a second—was this man one of those who were against him?

Unable to read the man's face, Cermeño barked out, "Well?" A Portuguese himself, although hired by the Spanish government in Mexico, the ship's captain did not trust the Spaniards under his command, and this sailor was Spanish.

The lookout saluted and gave his report. There was a small *ensenada* ahead, with two small islands off it.

Cermeño was jubilant. "Sail straight for the cove," he ordered the man at the wheel and went himself to study the instruments and chart the ship's course.

The *San Agustín* was about to enter the little bay between the coastline and the two islands, when the lookout shouted again.

"A-ho-oy! Ahoy below! Danger ahead!"

Cermeño turned from his instruments and once more yelled upward to find out what the danger was.

This time the lookout had sighted great rocks in the area where the ship would have to anchor if it were to rest in the shelter of the bay.

There was no help for it. The *San Agustín* had to bear away from land again. The darkness was growing thicker and the ship's rigging creaked and groaned ominously in the increasing wind. Huge waves began to batter the sides of the ship, and it was difficult to keep the vessel on its course.

Going into the officers' cabin for a moment's respite from the wind and salt water, Cermeño found the ship's chaplain, Fray Francisco de la Concepcion, kneeling before an improvised altar, holding a cross to his lips, and praying fervently that God would send them fair weather and proper winds, to make their journey back to Acapulco safe. They had been on the ocean many months, journeying to the Philippines and then back across this wild sea of the north with their cargo; now they were trying to find a safe harbor for the ships that carried on the trade with Manila, before returning to Mexico.

Cermeño opened his mouth to speak to the priest but changed his mind. Let the good Father pray. In the past hour the wind had grown to gale proportions. They would have need of prayers before this night was over.

The door to the officers' quarters opened again, and the boatswain came in behind Cermeño.

"The main mast has a rent in it, sir," he said, "and we have a new leak in the hull. What are your orders?"

Cermeño stood silent a moment. Then he said, "Order all men to their posts. We'll take in the sails. Our last soundings were fifteen fathoms." He went out of the cabin, fastening his jacket up around his neck and pulling his hat down over his face. The wind took him the instant he arrived on deck, and he was forced to grasp a mast to keep himself erect on the water-covered deck.

Cermeño was a brave and determined man but even he had a few qualms as to the number of hours left of life, either to him or his ship and men. Yet he was determined to do all he could to make his fortune by fulfilling the task given him by the Viceroy of New Spain, Luis de Velasco. His task, in that year of 1595, was to find harbors for galleons, like the one he commanded, so that they could rest the crews and repair the ships on their way home from the Orient. Acapulco was the chief port on the west coast of New Spain, and this was his eventual destination. But if he returned with no knowledge of new ports, his trials and labors would be as nothing, for he would receive no reward, nor would he be allowed any portion of the 130 tons of riches he carried.

The captain planted his feet firmly on the slippery deck, and went forward to issue orders to the man at the wheel, the boatswain in charge of the ship's rigging, and to the rest of his ship's crew, some of whom were Negro slaves, but many of whom had shipped with him of their own will. The ship's dog was curled up on a pile of line and Cermeño stooped to pet him as he went by. The rough hair was as wet as he, Cermeño, was.

It was ten o'clock. The sails must remain furled until the ship could drop anchor out of reach of any rocks. They were in bad condition. Cermeño stood near the helmsman, wishing he could hold the storm at bay at least

6

until morning, but only God could perform such miracles. He remained standing on the deck, watching the men on the rigging as the ropes swayed in the great wind.

Cermeño's ensign, Juan del Rio, came sliding across the deck to his captain. "The ship has sprung more leaks, sir," he said. "Water is pouring into the bilge at an alarming rate."

"Tell the men the pumps must be manned for two out of three watches," Cermeño said brusquely. Turning his back on his officer, he looked out once more across the furious sea. Then shouting at his second in command to keep watch on the ship proper, he climbed to the top of the main mast. He heard the frightened shouts and curses of his men far below him, but he ignored them. He clung to the masthead, a torn sail flapping in his ears underneath the sound of the storm. From his precarious perch, Cermeño was able to see farther ahead of his storm-tossed galleon than his lookouts could. Swinging wildly with the wind, the captain stayed on his dangerous perch until the *San Agustín* seemed safely beyond the threatening rocks. Calling out to his officers, he ordered the anchor dropped.

All through the night, the members of the crew of the *San Agustín* pumped water out of the depths of the hull. Other sailors hurried about the decks with lanterns, lashing down every bucket, mop, spare sail, or other object that might break loose and go overboard. Even the dog was taken below, out of the storm's fury.

The deck of the *San Agustín* was almost an open boat,

7

with only a small portion of it under cover. The common sailors slept in the hold, but that portion of the ship was now half water, with the many leaks, and they might as well have tried to sleep in a lake. When a man's turn to be relieved from duty came, he huddled on deck under whatever shelter he could find and tried to snatch a bit of sleep despite the terrifying wind and the loud groans and creakings of the ship.

With morning, the wind died. A pale sunlight shone on the north Pacific sea. The *San Agustín* had survived with all hands, but it was in very poor condition. Water continued to pour into the hull, and the entire hull was battered so that it seemed ready to break apart.

"We had better set sail and run with the wind, to home port," the boatswain said to Cermeño as the captain stood beside the wheel. "We will be fortunate, even so, to make it."

Cermeño did not answer, except with a grunt. He had no intention of setting out for Acapulco; he was determined, still, to land somewhere nearby. Originally, he had hoped to find a bay around the corner from the cape they had rounded two days before, Cape Mendocino, but the waters there were filled with rocks and the surf had looked dangerous. He now hoped to find a better port. Cermeño issued his commands. The *San Agustín* was to head back toward the coast, coming as near as was safe, and continue to hunt for a proper bay.

Later that day Gomez, the ship's scrivener, approached Cermeño as he rested briefly in the cabin. Gomez saluted

8

and handed a letter to Cermeño.

The letter began: "In view of the great danger in which the Captain and the Chief Pilot are putting the ship as she is very small and almost open . . ." and went on to demand that Cermeño proceed at once to Acapulco, it being impossible to pursue their mission with the ship in such a badly battered state.

The letter was signed by the second pilot, the master, and the boatswain.

Cermeño handed the letter back to Gomez.

"We will continue as planned," he said coldly. "So inform the officers and warn them that I will brook no rebellion. Remind them of the penalty for mutiny—the first man to be found guilty will be instantly executed."

Cermeño's firmness managed to keep the mutiny from erupting, but the ship's crew were anything but happy and wherever the captain went on board the vessel, dark looks followed him.

That afternoon, Cermeño saw a high ridge of land extending into the ocean. He swung the *San Agustin* around this point and found himself in a protected bay, with what looked like a river flowing into it. Here they could anchor, the captain believed.

Sebastian Cermeño landed in what is now Drake's Bay on the Pt. Reyes Peninsula on November 6, with winter almost upon him. He dropped anchor about four o'clock in the afternoon, in water to a depth of about forty feet, a mile and a half from shore. The harbor bottom was clean and full of sand. A group of natives had gathered on

9

shore when they saw the ship. From what Cermeño could see, the people were savages, wearing almost no clothing.

As the men on the *San Agustín* watched, an Indian jumped into a small craft made of the tule reeds and with a two-bladed oar, propelled himself swiftly through the water. As the Indian drew nearer, the men on the ship saw that he was naked except for a headdress of feathers and paint on his chest and arms.

Cermeño was aware of the tense silence of his men. It would take little to make them turn on him and try to force him to put out to sea again, he knew. He called out to the oncoming Indian, "Halt, or we shoot."

10

The Indian, not understanding the words, came on, giving small, cheerful yells. He had apparently taken the captain's words as a greeting, and Cermeño decided to hold his fire.

The Indian shot his agile craft forward until it was under the bow of the *San Agustín*. There he stood and delivered a long speech, keeping his craft from drifting by skillful use of his paddle. No one on board the galleon knew what the Indian was saying, but it seemed evident that he wished to be friendly. So Cermeño gave orders to supply the visitor with gifts from the ship's precious cargo. Cotton cloth, a handsome silk shirt, and a red cap were dropped overboard into the tule boat. After more speechmaking, the Indian returned to land, taking the gifts with him.

"Tomorrow," Cermeño told his men, "we shall return his visit."

INDIAN WELCOME

CAPTAIN CERMEÑO was eating his breakfast of pancakes made of flour and water and served with a tiny portion of the bacon that still remained in the *San Agustín's* larder when one of his crew called out, "They're coming back!"

Cermeño washed down his food with a small glass of wine and hurried on deck. Coming toward the ship were four separate Indian boats, each with a single Indian in it. As on the day before, the boats moved swiftly through the water. Cermeño watched, wondering if the Indian who had come the day before had gone back to his village to tell the other Indians about the strangers and to suggest an attack on the men from the ship, or if these Indians were coming only out of friendliness and curiosity. Or perhaps in the hope of receiving gifts. He went toward the railing of the ship's desk and called out a greeting as the first of the Indian canoes appeared below him.

13

"Hioh!" the Indians called back. This was a Miwok word for king or chief, but Cermeño knew only that the Indians seemed respectful in tone and manner. He ordered his men to drop cotton and taffeta cloth into the Indians' balsa canoes, and then the captain waved his visitors away, watching them return to shore before making plans to go ashore himself.

"Who is to go with you on shore?" Cermeño's ensign, Juan del Rio, asked when the ship's small boat was being lowered over the side of the ship.

Cermeño looked about him at his crew. Perhaps it was risky to leave behind on board the ship those officers who had earlier tried to force him to set sail for Acapulco. Still, these were chances a man had to take.

"You will come, of course," he said to the ensign. "And Officer Francisco de Chaves. And—" he named twenty-two men, seventeen of them harbusquiers carrying hooked guns. They and a sergeant, a corporal, three men bearing shields, and the designated officers were in the boat when it pulled away from the ship.

When the rowboat was a few yards from the *San Agustín*, Cermeño turned to look back at his ship. He was proud of the little vessel for having come through such stress and strain without breaking completely. The navigator, who had remained on board, lifted his arm in a salute meaning Godspeed on the mission ashore. Smiling, the Portuguese captain turned his face in the direction the boat was heading and looked to the unknown shore.

The fog that had curled around the headland and had

14

hung over the coastline all morning, was lifting. As the ship's men brought the rowboat into the shallow water at the edge of the sand, Cermeño stepped out, wading through a few feet of the ocean to reach solid land. What a fair place this was. Not far away a spit of sand thrust itself into the water and from somewhere a bird sang sweetly, as if in welcome. Cermeño remembered having heard that it was in this part of the world that the English sea captain, Sir Francis Drake, had found a good harbor. Perhaps it was this very place! The Englishman, it was said, had hauled his leaky vessel onto shore and mended it before setting forth again. Cermeño knew little of Drake except that he was the same Englishman who had helped to destroy the ships of the Spanish war fleet, the Invincible Armada. Some of those ships had been set afire while still in the harbor at Calais—it was a story told by Spanish sailors everywhere.

However, there seemed no evidence here of any other white man's visit, so Cermeño preferred to believe he was the first. Even if Drake had been there once, he, Cermeño, working for a Spanish king, would take the harbor and the land around it in the name of the country that employed and trusted him. His dream was to return to Portugal a rich man, respected by all both for his wealth and for his courage and his adventures in the wild unknown world that few men had seen.

The place where the sailors beached the ship's boat was a long gunshot from the village of the Indians, although the village could be plainly seen from the entrance to the

estero, or estuary. Before marching on to the village, Cermeño took possession of the land and the harbor in the name of "the King, our master."

"It shall be called *La Baya de San Francisco,*" he announced. "Come, Fray Francisco, let us baptize it."

The friar, a member of the Order of the Franciscans, knelt down on the shore and scooping handfuls of the ocean water, spilled it on the land, saying, "I baptize this land and this *ensenada* in the name of the Lord Most Holy." The barefoot priest then knelt and put his lips to the ground he had declared sacred.

"Now we will march to the village," said Cermeño. "Raise the banner, Lieutenant."

Juan del Rio raised the banner he had brought from the *San Agustín,* the banner that proclaimed the ship to be the property of the King of Spain. Cermeño walked with the standard bearer, as did the priest, flanked on both sides by the harbusquiers with their guns. No one spoke, but every man kept tight watch on the surrounding landscape.

When the men from the ship reached the Indian village on the shores of the four-armed *estero,* they stopped and waited to see what the people of the village would do.

"The men are naked, Captain!" the priest exclaimed, looking shocked.

Cermeño said softly, "They know no better, Father." But he wondered a little at their ability to resist the cool, foggy wind. It was then November 7 and the sun was pale. He saw that the Indian women were more fully clothed than the men. Most of the women wore some kind of skirt made from reeds and many had an animal skin hanging down over the upper portion of their bronze-colored bodies. Both the men and the women wore their hair long, nearly to their shoulders, and the men were beardless, unlike the ship's officers. The Indian men held bows in their hands and quivers full of arrows were slung around their waists. Above the skin bag of arrows, the breasts of the men were painted in bright colors, as were also their arms.

"They seem well-fed," Officer Chaves murmured to Cermeño. Meals had been spare for a long time on board the *San Agustín.* The ruddy-skinned natives were strongly built, with firm-looking muscles and solid flesh on their bones. It hardly seemed likely that the Indians had any difficulty finding food.

None of the Indians attempted to stop the advance of the white men. They waited silently as the procession moved through the village, behaving a little as if gods

18

had come into their world. Cermeño, relaxing his watch-fulness, took time to look around him. He noted that the Indian houses were built of long reeds like those the women wore, or else of wood that must have drifted onto shore from the sea. Poles of bushes and sticks of driftwood were set so they leaned against each other and rushes covered the spaces between the poles.

As the white men proceeded through the little village, many of the villagers, especially the women and children, disappeared inside their huts. At the entrance to the main hut of the village stood an Indian whose limbs and body were naked except for a loose covering of brilliant feathers. This Indian did not disappear; he stood firm as the strangers approached his home. He said something in his own language, but again none of the Spaniards under-stood him. Then, suddenly, Cermeño recognized the In-dian. He was the man who had come out alone to the ship the day before. His was the largest hut in the village, Cermeño saw. He must be the king.

In Spanish, Cermeño tried to make clear his admira-tion for the village and its people, smiling and using signs as he spoke. After a minute or two the Indian chief gave an order to one of the men who stood with him. The man disappeared and came back carrying a basket in which there were some seeds. The chief held the basket out to Cermeño, indicating that he should take some of the seeds. Cermeño, not knowing if the seeds were meant to be food, poison, or perhaps magic medicine, neverthe-less felt it was necessary to accept the Indian's offer. He took one of the seeds, which was shaped like an anise seed, and bit into it. After a second of chewing, Cermeño turned to his companions.

"It tastes very like our sesame," he said.

Later, the sailors saw Indian women pounding the seeds into flour and learned that a kind of flat bread was made from the flour. The seed came from a variety of *godetia*, a plant sometimes called Farewell-to-Spring. The plant grew on the slopes of the hills that could be seen from the village, and when the seeds appeared the Indians harvested them and stored them until they needed them.

The men from the ship continued to move around the Indian village, those carrying guns keeping an eye out for any unfriendly sign from the villagers. Cermeño also kept an eye out. He wanted to learn what he could of these strange savages in order to make a full report to Luis de Velasco at Acapulco.

The huts of the villagers seemed to be built partly below ground. Stopping by one of the huts to examine it more closely, Cermeño was invited inside by the Indian whose home it apparently was. At least that was how Cermeño interpreted the man's gesture toward the entrance to the hut. The Indian, seeing Cermeño's hesitation, himself led the way through the opening that was the hut's door.

Cermeño, following, found himself in a tentlike structure with a small fire burning in the center of the room. No smoke hole was visible; the smoke drifted toward the open doorway although much of it remained inside the hut. Cermeño controlled a cough and stepped out.

Outside the hut, women were seated cross-legged around a larger fire, watching over large baskets set on hot stones at the edge of the flames. On the opposite side of the fire, an Indian girl stirred the ashes with great care. As Cermeño watched, one of the women pulled a large crab from a pile of moist seaweed beside the fire and holding the creature suspended on a long stick, dropped it into a basket that contained water. A little of the water leaked out of the basket, but the grasses from which it had been made were so tightly woven together it was almost waterproof.

Turning to look out at the great ocean visible through the space between the cliffs at the edge of the *estero,* Cermeño thought how rich the waters, both of the inlet from the sea, and the sea itself, must be.

He tried to ask the girl who was stirring the ashes of the fire what she was doing but she only answered *Tculu,* even when he went through a pantomime of pointing to the ashes and frowning questioningly. Suddenly the Indian girl looked shyly at the visitor and took up a branched stick. With it she pulled something from the ashes. *Tculu* she said again. The word must mean *acorn,* Cermeño decided, because what she pulled from the fire was an acorn. She had been roasting them in the ashes. He could see no oak trees in the village nor along the shores of the *estero,* but probably the Indians went long distances, to where there were trees and other growing plants, to gather food.

"They need for very little," Cermeño commented to the priest beside him. "They have food of all kinds near at hand. Or so it seems." He waved his hand toward the ridge of a distant hill. A band of elk or deer was moving slowly along the ridge, stopping to graze now and then. "With their bows and arrows, the Indians can get meat whenever they wish, if they know how to hunt, and the skins of the dead animals will keep them warm."

"They do not know God," the Franciscan father said sorrowfully. "No man is without need when he has not been baptized in the name of our Most Holy Lord."

"True, true," Cermeño murmured.

The men of the *San Agustín* decided that there must have been a big hunt sometime not too long before they came. Deer horns lay bleaching on the sandy soil at the edge of the *estero*. The Indians used the horns for tools and ornaments. Cermeño picked up a pair of horns that struck his eye and measured them with his hands. He found they measured sixteen palms from tip to tip. For a man from Portugal, this seemed a very large species of deer. Cermeño decided to take the horns back to Acapulco with him.

Cermeño and his companions were about to leave the village and explore the surrounding countryside when they caught sight of a band of Indians about a mile from them. The Indians were filing down a trail, heading straight toward Cermeño and his men. They came on the run, yelling "Hooaahoohoo! Hooaahoohoo!" It was almost a scream, and their headgear, made of black plumes that waved ferociously as the men danced back and forth in a zigzag fashion across the path, was frightening. Sometimes they pranced around in a circle, throwing back their heads to give out with howls worse than those of wild beasts.

Cermeño ordered the harbusquiers to hold themselves ready to fire at his command, but not a second before. He meantime planted his feet firmly on the ground at the edge of the village, instructing his ensign to hold the Spanish banner high, straight, and unwavering. Then he waited.

The Indians, seeing that the band of white men were not running away, also halted. For a short time the two parties faced each other about twenty feet apart. Cermeño could hear the Indians talking to one another, and he tried to distinguish from the tone of their voices just how dangerous they might be. He caught sounds like "O," or "Yo," but he couldn't be sure whether these yells meant peace or war. In his mind was the clear knowledge that, despite the arms his men carried, the Indians might well take them captive. Their arrows were strong and sharply pointed. The arrowheads he had seen in the village were made of stone, the edges of which had been flaked to a sharpness he did not care to think about. Sunk into a man's breast, such arrowheads could kill, could make blood run out onto the ground.

After some throbbing moments of inaction, Cermeño and his officers decided they must either shoot or run.

23

Cermeño started to give a command to his harbusquiers when he saw one of the approaching Indians step out in front of the others. The solitary Indian bore a tall banner of black feathers. His long hair was gathered into a bunch at the back of his head and from his hair bunch the plumes of many feathers jutted out. Single feathers, like horns, also thrust out towards the front of his head. His arms and his breast were painted black and red and he wore a tunic of rabbit skins.

Some of the Indians from the village had followed the men from the ship on their way out of the village, and now one of these, a man who had behaved with great friendliness toward the visitors, stepped toward the man with the feather banner. He made a speech, pointing first toward the white men and making signs, then pointing to the bows that the advancing Indians had been holding poised, with the strings taut. It took several speeches but finally the Indians put down their bows and arrows. The man who carried the feather banner walked up to Cermeño and gave the banner to him.

The captain of the *San Agustín* drew a relieved breath. The Indians wanted to be friends. Taking off his bright taffeta sash, he offered it to the Indian in exchange for the banner. The other Indians, those who had carried the bows, began to chatter excitedly among themselves. Cermeño told some of his men to take off their sashes, also, and pass them over to the Indians. This began an exchange of gifts that brought smiles to the faces of the men from the ship. When the Indians were given the sashes,

24

they brought their bows and arrows to Cermeño. Cermeño thanked them with a deep bow and passed the weapons to his men, noting as he did that some of the arrows were beautifully designed.

There was no more trouble or threat of trouble from any of the Indians after that. The small band of sailors and officers climbed to the top of a nearby hill to see if there were other villages or settlements nearby. At the top of the hill they met an Indian man and woman. The woman was carrying a child. As the group of white men came close to the Indian couple, the father held out a basket of acorns. Cermeño, touched by this free will offering, turned to his men and said, "Let no one of you harm this man or his family, or deprive them of anything that belongs to them. They have of their own accord offered food to strangers and for that I honor and respect them."

Although the Indian man and woman understood none of the words that Cermeño spoke, they seemed to understand that the white men were friends and they insisted on walking with the men from the *San Agustín* around the hill and back down again to the beach on the *estero*.

When they reached the beach, Cermeño sat down on the sand.

"We will build a camp at this place," he told his men, "to make an entrenchment for our defense." He glanced at the Indian couple and then back toward the village they had visited. "These people seem very friendly, but we must be careful and not tempt them to do us harm." He then ordered that planks and a hollowed-out tree trunk the *San Agustín* had carried be brought from the ship and taken to the spot he had chosen. The planks and the tree trunk were to be assembled into a *lanche* or launch with which he planned to explore the coast in the hope of finding other good harbors. "The launch must be built as soon as possible, so we can go about fulfilling our mission," he said. The ship's boat that had brought them to shore from the ship was too small for exploring.

While some of his men returned to the ship to carry out Cermeño's orders, the captain remained on shore. From time to time his gaze roamed the waters of the *estero,* watching the gulls sitting at the edge of the water looking for food, or studying the flight of other birds drifting high above. He wondered if Drake might have stood on this same spot sixteen years earlier. If so, Cermeño thought, Drake should have planted a flag or some

other emblem to declare his country's ownership of the place. Since he had not, it had now been claimed for Spain. Let the Queen, Elizabeth of England, and the Spanish monarch, Philip, fight it out if the time ever came when this harbor and the lands around it should be of importance.

Cermeño was roused from these speculations by visitors. First one Indian and then another came to speak to him, each one making a long speech, of which the Portuguese captain understood little. Finally, the big chief, the one who had come first to the ship, appeared. He made an even longer speech than the one he had delivered the day before, making signs with his hands and bobbing his headdress in various directions. Cermeño listened carefully, understanding from its tone that the speech was friendly. When the chief had finished talking, the ship's captain gave him more pieces of silk and cotton, indicating that he would like the Indians to go away and leave

the white men alone for a while, so that they could do their work. It took a lot of sign language and waving of hands, but finally the last of the Indians disappeared, going toward the village with many backward looks.

AN OPEN BOAT

IN THE DAYS THAT FOLLOWED the setting up of a camp on the shore of the bay in which the *San Augustin* was anchored, the men went back and forth between ship and shore. They always left men on guard at the camp, not fully trusting the Indians. The men who slept on shore found the nights there no more uncomfortable than many they had spent on board the *San Agustin* in stormy weather. There were few complaints. In the daytime, work on the launch proceeded well.

Some trouble developed with the Indians when the parts for the launch were first put on shore. One of the Spanish officers caught an Indian stealing away from the camp with wood that was intended for the launch.

The officer ran after the Indian and grabbed an end of the plank. "Let go, you thief!" he shouted at the Indian in Spanish.

The Indian began to howl, refusing to let go of the piece of lumber. Hearing his yells, other Indians appeared over the hill that lay between Cermeño's camp and the village. As they came closer, Cermeño saw that they were carrying bows and arrows. He ordered the harbusquiers who were on guard to shoulder their guns and stand ready. Then he planted himself in front of the camp, crossing his arms and assuming an attitude of authority and sternness.

The officer and the Indian continued to wrestle over the stolen plank until, suddenly, the Indian let go and ran to join his friends. The officer who had been struggling with him fell onto the sand with the plank, but seeing how hostile the oncoming group of Indians were, he left the lumber where it was and ran back toward the camp. He had nearly reached its protection when an arrow sang through the air and he fell to the ground.

A couple of his comrades ran to him. They managed to pull out the arrow, which had not gone in deep, although blood spilled over his uniform. The men who had rescued him tore off his tunic and began to try to staunch the flow of blood. One of them examined the wound left by the arrow.

"I don't think it is too grave a wound," he said. "Are you feeling better?" he asked the wounded man.

The officer nodded and with the help of his men struggled to his feet and walked back to where Cermeño and the others were waiting anxiously.

Cermeño ordered his soldiers to follow the Indians.

"Let them know we will tolerate no thievery," he said. "Gifts we have gladly given them, of whatever we have in abundance, but none are to help themselves to our stores."

The soldiers started to run toward the group of Indians who seemed undecided as to whether to keep coming toward the white men or not. The sight of the pursuing soldiers made up their minds. They turned and ran, leaving behind them a sack and a half of acorns, which the harbusquiers took back to camp.

Cermeño was puzzled when he saw the acorns. Had the Indians started out to make him a gift of the nuts and been frightened by the yells of the man who had stolen the wood? He dipped his hand into the sack and brought out a handful of nuts. Cracking one, he bit into the center meat, making a sour face after he tasted it.

The meat was bitter; one of his men told him that the Indians knew how to treat the acorns to make them taste better. At least that was what the sailor had figured out from seeing the women working on the acorn harvest in the village, and from the few Indian words he thought he had understood. Like the seeds Cermeño had seen in the village, the acorns were pounded into flour by the Indian women and bread was made from them.

When there was time, Cermeño decided, he would visit the village again and learn more about the food the Indians ate. The diet on board ship was lacking in fresh meat and the fruit of plants. Looking at the hills in the distance, brown now but perhaps green in the spring, he felt a yearning for fresh food. In a few days, he would take a party of men and explore the coastline, going inland when possible, to roam the countryside also. Perhaps this fair land would someday be a place where men from Spain and Portugal would come and build a new, rich country.

The task of putting the launch together was not easy in spite of the fact that the parts for it had been prepared before the *San Agustín* left Manila. The boat would have to be propelled through the water by means of sweeps— oars much longer than those used for ship's rowboat— and these had to be shaped by hand. Cermeño had extra canvas brought from the ship and with it he made a tent, using the Indians' method of leaning together poles made from branches of trees as a frame. Most of the men who slept at the camp lay on open ground, but Cermeño and his chief officer, Francisco de Chaves, made the improvised tent their headquarters.

"When the launch is ready," Cermeño said to de Chaves, "we will use this piece of canvas for a sail." He glanced up at the tent sides. The plan for the launch included two square sails, but Cermeño felt that one would do, since the explorations were to be made close to shore. It was necessary to be sparing of all supplies, he had learned.

Only a skeleton crew was left on board the *San Agustín* while the men on shore proceeded with their tasks. A ship at anchor needed little attention, and Cermeño's plan for exploring the land and coast meant he needed men to accompany him, and others to guard the camp.

On the fifteenth of November, nine days after the *San Agustín* had dropped anchor in the bay, Captain Cermeño took eight of his soldiers, plus the scrivener, on an exploring trip. The launch still not being completed, they used the ship's rowboat.

"Take careful note of all that we find," Cermeño instructed the scrivener, whose job it was to write down everything needed to make a report to the authorities at Acapulco. In the rowboat, the exploring crew followed what they thought was an arm of a river but might have been an inlet from the *estero*. They found the adjoining countryside of great interest because trees and shrubs and many different kinds of animals were to be seen. Other Indian villages were located farther inland, and the people were as friendly to the strange white men as the first group on the *estero* shores. Cermeño reported, when he returned to camp after this brief trip, that water good for drinking could be found by digging down a little way anyplace where there were sandbanks near the sea.

For the next fifteen days, the weather was calm and pleasant. The men of the *San Agustín* continued exploring the area around the bay they had named the Bay of San Francisco. They made many journeys on foot and others in the rowboat, while the galleon itself stood at anchor, unused. One of Cermeño's officers suggested that the *San Agustín* should be brought closer inside the protected bay, but Cermeño, who did not like criticism, said sharply, "There is no reason to move the anchors. The sea is quiet and our ship is safe enough where it is. Do you want the Indians to be slipping out there at night to ransack the ship and perhaps murder the crew?"

Cermeño's stubbornness and poor judgment were disastrous. Out of the southwest, with the suddenness of a summer squall, gale winds struck the coast.

Cermeño was inside his improvised tent when he heard the first whistle of the wind and felt the canvas billow around him.

"Chaves!" he called, striding out into the wind. "We must get out to the ship! Hear that wind?"

"It's a sou-wester, sir," Chaves said as the two officers plowed through the sand toward the water's edge, where the rowboat was anchored. The storm had made the afternoon dark and as the storm increased, rolling up huge black clouds all over the sky, so did the darkness.

"Someone must put out in the boat and go to the rescue of the men on board ship!" Cermeño yelled to his companion. He shouted commands to the men in the encampment, and some of them began to run toward the little boat, rocking fiercely in the shallow water as the waves raced inland toward it.

"It's no use, Captain!" one of the men reported after a hopeless struggle to launch the rowboat. "No one could make it to the ship in the boat. She's already tossing like a feather out there." He waved toward the dim shape of the galleon, rolling in the increasingly large waves.

"I'll take the boat out alone!" Cermeño said angrily, marching toward the rowboat where the men had

34

dragged it higher onto the beach, trying to keep it out of reach of the rocking waves. But as he and two other men reached the boat, a wave higher than their heads rolled in off the sea. Cermeño, with his companions, was forced to turn and run back the way they had come. When the huge wave receded, the rowboat was gone, taken out to sea by the wave.

"There are only a dozen men aboard the ship," Cermeño said, his voice harsh with strain. "God help them all! It will be a miracle if she can ride out this storm with such a small crew to handle her." He would have asked the priest to pray for the *San Agustín* except that the good father was himself on board the tossing vessel. Instead, he and his officers began to mutter prayers that seemed almost like curses as they peered through the storm to try to see what was happening to their ship.

"She's broken loose!" a man yelled suddenly. "She'll go down for sure."

Cermeño groaned. Above the sound of the crash and boom of surf pounding against the white cliffs at the edge of the bay, and the lion roar of the wind, he listened anxiously for the sound of splintering wood. It came. The galleon had cracked. It was being hit by wave after giant wave, each one battering the floundering vessel, driving it hard toward shore. Above the sound of the sea, Cermeño heard screams—the men were being tossed into the sea like pebbles. He covered his face with his hands. There was no way to rescue the helpless men as long as the storm raged. Even when it quieted, who could hope for anything except dead bodies in such a boiling ocean? The men around him were silent and it seemed to Cermeño that the silence was an ominous one, more ominous than the storm itself. If the men mutinied, he would be at their mercy.

"Come!" he ordered, "let us return to camp. There is nothing to be done here until the storm is over."

He started off, his ears pitched to hear if the men followed him. After only a moment, all did. There would be no mutiny, Cermeño thought with relief. He was still the commander of the crew that had sailed with him on the *San Agustín*. They would make their way southward somehow, and he would be in command. He had no ship, a dozen of his men were drowned, and his precious cargo of porcelain, fine silks, and beeswax was gone, but he was still Captain Sebastian Cermeño.

In the morning, the seas having calmed, the men from the ship, along with many Indians, watched soberly as pieces of the *San Agustín* washed ashore. Cermeño walked to a place where a heap of tangled cloth had been dumped by a wave. Plucking at the cloth, he drew out a length of taffeta that shone brilliantly in its wetness, but was ruined for sale to traders. The cloth was torn in many places and the colors had run. One of the other men picked up something else. It was a fragment of the rare china the ship had carried, the most valuable portion of the cargo that was to have made Sebastian Cermeño a rich man. With an oath, Cermeño threw the broken china toward the sea, and going back to camp, began to issue orders to his men. The ship's dog, which had been tied to a portion of the launch to keep it from being caught by the waves at the water's edge, began a furious barking as the men reappeared.

"We still have our mascot," Cermeño said, untying the animal and patting its head to quiet it. He went on, "Captain Chaves will stay here and supervise the finishing of the launch. We have no choice now but to make the launch seaworthy; it is our only hope of reaching home." He turned to some of the other men. "You, de Morgana, Sergeant de Gutierrez, Hernandes—" Cermeño called out a list of names, "are to come with me to hunt for food." What food that had remained on board ship was of course lost. The crew, or what was left of it, would have to survive off whatever native foods could be found.

Besides Cermeño, eleven Spaniards, a few armed slaves, all of whom were black men, and some Indians set out on foot to hunt for food. They found another Indian village about eight or nine miles from their camp. This village was on a branch of a creek. On the banks of the stream were many trees and shrubs from which the men collected acorns and hazelnuts, madrone berries, and fra-

grant herbs. They were also able to shoot partridge and deer, which they took back to their camp. Not having the skills of the Indians in curing the meat of wild game, they ate the birds and deer meat immediately, saving only the skins of the deer for additional clothing in case colder weather should come.

The launch was finally finished and on December 8, the ocean calm, the *San Buenaventura*, as Cermeño had named the launch, was shoved from the beach into the shallow water. Seventy men and the ship's dog were crowded into the deckless, open boat. Cermeño would have left the dog behind but the men of the crew grumbled at this, so he gave in. He expected trouble enough with his men before this crude ship had made its way along the thousands of miles to the home port. Several of his men had already run off, escaping on foot over the hills, probably hoping to find a life with the Indians that was more pleasant than life on the open sea.

With the Indians watching from shore, the launch began its long journey, a journey that ended with only a handful of men still alive. The dog did not survive; the starving men on the rude boat finally had to kill and eat the animal to save themselves. The *San Buenaventura* arrived at Acapulco two months after it left Drake's Bay. Captain Cermeño had failed his mission, which was to find new and safe harbors along the northern California coast for the Manila galleons that sailed the seas trading the treasures of the Orient for Mexican silver.

For one hundred and seventy years after Cermeño and his men sailed away from Point Reyes in the launch, no other white man is known to have set foot on the peninsula. The Spaniards later sent another excursion northwards from Acapulco on the same kind of mission. This excursion, consisting of three ships, was headed by Sebastian Vizcaino. One of Vizcaino's officers had been with Cermeño in 1595. He recognized Drake's Bay and the headland around which the *San Agustín* had come seven years earlier. Vizcaino made no effort to enter the bay itself but he named the point of land jutting out into the ocean *Punta de los Reyes,* meaning Point of the Kings, because the day he rounded the headland was January 6, 1603, and January 6 was celebrated by the Spaniards as the Feast of the Three Kings of the Nativity.

If Francis Drake brought his ship, *The Golden Hinde,* on shore at Drake's Bay in 1579, sixteen years before Cermeño anchored the *San Agustín* at the edge of the *estero,* no one has proved it yet. An Englishman, George Vancouver, believing that Drake had landed on the Point Reyes peninsula, named the bay for his fellow countryman. Originally called the Sir Francis Drake Bay by Vancouver, it was later shortened to Drake's Bay, the name it bears today.

THE MIWOK
AND THE MISSION

WHETHER FRANCIS DRAKE or Sebastian Cermeño was the first white man to land on the shores of the Point Reyes coastal area, it was the Spaniards who first settled the surrounding land. Priests and soldiers came to convert the natives they found living in what the priests called heathen nakedness, and a mission was founded by the Franciscan fathers who had come up from Mexico. The mission was named the Mission San Rafael Arcangel; it was built in 1817 as an assistant mission to the larger one in San Francisco across the bay.

One of the soldiers whose job it was to guard the Mission and to bring back Indians who ran off from their labors in the orchards and grounds of the Mission, was Rafael Garcia. Garcia arrived at the mission three years after it had been built and in those three years most of the Indians from the Miwok villages had come or been

40

brought into the mission.

One morning Garcia was sent to the Point Reyes peninsula in search of an Indian who, ungrateful to the priests for having given him a new God and for teaching him new and useful skills, had disappeared. Riding swiftly through the high grass of the wild oats, up and down the rolling hills and along the ridge that divided the peninsula, Garcia studied the landscape. In the distance he caught glimpses of the ocean and remembered that the Indians had once hunted the sea otter that

floated on beds of kelp near the coast. Otter hunting had been dangerous in the fragile canoes the Indians built, but it had been a free life and an exciting one, Garcia supposed. Pelts of otter made beautiful warm robes. Perhaps he might own such a robe himself someday.

The runaway that Garcia was looking for was named Miguel, having been so baptized by Father Juan Amoroso. Miguel had great skill with a bow and arrow and that made him dangerous. Miguel had been a member of a tribe that had lived in a village on the edge of the *estero*. That was the reason Garcia was looking for the deserter on the Point Reyes peninsula.

Garcia came to a high place that looked down over the Pacific. The sea was rolling green, transparent logs of water inland and smashing them against the sandstone cliffs. He loved the sea. Where he had been born, in the country around the mission of San Diego, he had often stood beside the ocean and let its breezes cool him. He watched the waves for a second, thinking of the time long before when a Spanish ship had been wrecked on the shores of this very place. The tale of the wreck and of the Indians who had lived in the crude villages beside the *estero* that he would reach in a few minutes had been told to him by a priest in San Diego, before he came north.

It was a brilliant autumn day. During the night rain had washed the dust from the leaves of the trees and plants, leaving the air fresh and the foliage bright. A meadowlark was perched on an enormous thistle beside a toyon bush. It chortled a few melodious phrases, its yellow breast flashing as it sang. Then it suddenly left its perch, made a few sharp strokes on the air, and sailed off over the edge of the hill, toward the sea.

The berries on the toyon were not yet ripe, but when the Feast of the Nativity arrived, they would be red as fire. Each year the priests sent Indian converts to gather branches of the ripe berries for use in decorating the chapel of the Mission. The wooden beam outside the chapel, from which the Mission bell was suspended, would be decorated with leaves and berries, too.

Garcia and his horse pounded along an Indian trail that led to the *estero*. In the distance he could see the point of land called Punta de los Reyes, which protected the bay and the *estero* from ocean storms, at least the worst of them. Closer at hand a band of elk was feeding.

The soldier started to urge his horse forward at a faster pace but he caught sight of what looked like a small, slowly moving elk or deer. Suspicious, Garcia was about to lift his musket when he saw the creature pull a bow from behind a bush and fit an arrow into it. Miguel! It must be Miguel. The man was crawling on all fours, pretending to eat grass as though he were himself a deer. On his head was tied the head of a dead stag.

In the days before their conversion, many Indians had hunted elk this way. Now the Indians ate beef from the cattle they helped the Mission fathers to raise and had little incentive to hunt. Before the Mission time, however, they had lived entirely off wild game. Also, what little clothing they had worn had been made of animal skins, especially elk and rabbit. Garcia decided to wait until Miguel had killed his deer before trying to capture the Indian. He would be more easily taken when he ran to examine his kill.

While the soldier watched, the Indian took several more arrows from the quiver at his waist and let them fly into the deer herd. Two of the animals dropped to the ground, the others bounded swiftly off into some trees where they could conceal themselves better.

Rafael Garcia once more dug his spurs into his horse's sides. Yelling an order to halt at the surprised Indian, he galloped across a small swamp and pointed his musket at Miguel's head. "Untie that filthy object," he ordered, pointing at the stag's head that had been the Indian's disguise for the deer.

For a second it looked as if Miguel would refuse. He glanced at his bow, which he had placed on the ground after shooting his arrows. But even if he could have snatched it up swiftly, there was only one arrow left in his quiver. Besides, before he could fit that arrow to his bow, the soldier's gun would have shot his arm from his side. Sullenly the Indian began to untie the animal head, letting his own black hair fall down around his ears.

"Now hand me that arrow," commanded the soldier, keeping his gun trained on his victim.

Miguel slowly pulled his remaining arrow from the quiver and handed it to Garcia. It was hopeless to rebel. If he made a move, he would be shot.

The soldier unwound a length of rope from his saddle

horn without taking his gun off Miguel. He tied the Indian's hands behind his back and made him walk in front of him and his horse until they reached the nearly abandoned Indian village by the *estero*. There Garcia searched the few dilapidated huts, which were all that remained of the village, for traces of other deserting Indians, but there was no one.

Hoisting the captured and trussed Miguel onto the back of his horse, the Spanish soldier remounted and galloped back to the Mission. Above the grass where the two slain deer lay, three turkey vultures circled. When the birds were certain that the deer were dead, they would swoop to feast on the raw flesh.

The journey to return a runaway was not the first visit that Rafael Garcia made to the peninsula of land that lay between the long arm of the Pacific known as Tomales Bay and the rugged outer coast, nor was it to be his last. His visits convinced him that he would like to live on the peninsula and raise many cattle and many children, although at the time he first dreamed of it, he was not yet married and received little pay. He could hope, however, that if he was a good soldier for his government, he might receive a reward. It might even be a few acres of land.

The year of the return of Miguel by Rafael Garcia was 1820. By then the Mission San Rafael Arcangel was no longer only an *asistencia,* or auxiliary, to the Mission Dolores in San Francisco, it was a mission in its own right. With the help of the Indians they had converted,

the padres of the mission raised horses and cattle, culti-
vated wheat, beans, barley, and maize. They raised grapes
and figs in their vineyards and orchards and the religious
settlement thrived during the first years of its existence,
while California was part of Mexico and belonged to
Spain. But in 1821 the people of Mexico rebelled and
overthrew the Spanish kings to make their land a re-
public.

Then the Mexican government made plans to create
towns of the Mission settlements. The time of the dons
and padres, of Spanish land grants so large that ordinary
men lived like rulers of kingdoms and the priests' rule
was law to the Indian natives, was passing away. By 1834,
the Indians were freed from the control of the priests and
were told they could return to their villages if they
wished. But many of the villages had fallen into ruin, and
many of the Indians had died from white men's diseases.
Those who had survived no longer knew how to live off
fish and shellfish, wild seeds and berries, or to hunt game
as their forefathers had done. Few of them even knew
how to make a good bow, or arrows, suitable for hunting
elk, or remembered how to catch the long-eared hares
that had once been so important a part of the Indian's
diet.

By 1842, eight years after the California missions were
taken over by the Mexican government, there were only
twenty members of the original Indian tribes in the vi-
cinity of the San Rafael Mission. The remaining Marin
County Indians were widely scattered over the country

46

and totaled only about 1400 in all. An agent for the Indians, appointed by the government, gathered together these remnants of the people that had, hundreds of years earlier, greeted Sebastian Cermeño and perhaps even Sir Francis Drake, on the shores of Drake's Bay. The Indian agent, Timoteo Murphy, helped the Miwok establish themselves on an inland ranch where they lived for many years. But eventually the Indians again scattered, some securing employment on the early ranchos, some wandering about, often in ragged clothing, some ending their lives living on welfare assistance.

The Coast Miwok had lived in what one anthropologist has called a kind of paradise, until the white man came. And when the Indians were gone, the white man took over. Not long after the missions had lost their lands, the new Mexican government made grants of land on the Point Reyes peninsula to individuals who had assisted in the overthrow of Spain, or as a reward for other services. The first of these grants on the peninsula was to James Richard Berry, who, in 1836, was given 35,000 acres of land in what is now the Olema Valley portion of the Seashore. Berry named his grant the Rancho Punta de los Reyes; it became the first ranch on Point Reyes peninsula. Later, Berry sold part of his grant to an English sea captain, Joseph F. Snook, who built a cabin beside the trail that led from Point Reyes headland to Tomales Bay. That cabin was the first building to be erected by a white man on the Point Reyes peninsula.

As for the soldier who helped to defend the Mission

from hostile Indians and was sent out to capture run-aways, Rafael Garcia, he, too, received land from the Mexican government. In time, he fulfilled his dream of raising a family within sound of the beautiful Pacific, and the name Garcia appears often in records of the period when California was on its way to becoming one of the United States of America.

WILD HORSE ROUNDUP

THE MIWOK INDIANS who were employed on the ranches of northern California were among the most fortunate of their tribe. One such couple was an Indian cowboy, or *vaquero,* Nicolas, and his wife, Juanita. They worked on a Point Reyes rancho that belonged to a San Francisco lawyer, Oscar Shafter, but was leased to a man who raised cattle. The *rancho,* the Punta de los Reyes, held annual roundups of cattle and wild horses and Oscar Shafter arrived for a visit on the day of the wild horse roundup.

On the morning of the roundup, the Indian woman, Juanita, came out of the kitchen entrance to the adobe ranch house carrying a tray of loaves of bread to be baked in the outdoor oven of rocks plastered together with adobe mud. Her long, loose skirt switched around her ankles and her sandals slapped against the hard-packed dirt. In the corral beyond, Nicolas and the other *vaqueros* were getting ready to ride out on the range.

Juanita and Nicolas had been given their names by the priests at the Mission. Neither of them remembered much about that time—they had left the Mission while they were still children. Juanita had gone with her family to a *rancho* near the Mission, where she had been taught to grind corn and make bread by the mistress of the rancho and by her mother. Nicolas was a *mestizo*, half-Spanish and half-Indian. He had long ago forgotten, if he ever knew, what had happened to his parents, except that they were both supposed to be dead. He did not remember them. Nicolas had grown up with the children of a rancher and had learned many useful things, especially how to raise, ride, and care for horses.

Sometimes Juanita's mother, who was very old now and spent nearly all her time sitting in the sun near the ranch house where she had once worked, told Juanita's children of the old days at the Mission, of the good padre who had loved children and had carried grapes and figs around in the wide sleeves of his gray robe for them. But Nicolas and Juanita were not interested in those days. It had been so long ago, over thirty years, and now they had children of their own.

Juanita set the tray of unbaked bread on a table beside the oven and bent down to peer inside. The fire had been going for over an hour. It should be hot enough for the bread. She wanted to get the baking done early, so there would be fresh loaves when Mr. Shafter arrived from San Francisco.

The trip from the city was a long and tiring one in those days. The traveler had to take a steamer from the city to Point San Quentin, and a wagon from there to San Rafael. After that he had to come on horseback another twenty miles. Anyone who made such a journey would welcome fresh bread and newly churned butter. Juanita closed the oven door and returned to the house. The bread would be ready in good time.

The ocean could not be seen from the ranch house but its misty odor drifted to Juanita's nostrils, brought by the breezes that blew inland. The day before had been heavy with fog but the fog was lifting early this morning. There was fog most mornings from early May until the rains came in November or December. The fog was good for the pasture land, where the cattle grazed, but Juanita was always glad when the sun burned it off or the wind drove it away.

Somewhere off across the water was the city of San Francisco, about which Juanita had heard much but to which she had never been. Nicolas had been there more than once and had told Juanita she would not like it. "The city is dirty and noisy. Rough men roam the streets, miners and peddlers and wicked women are all around. It is better to stay here in the country. In San Francisco there is nothing to do, no horses to ride, no fish to catch, not a single elk to be seen anywhere. The city is no place for an Indian woman."

Juanita had heard about the finding of gold in other parts of California and of the people who had flocked there from everywhere to hunt for it. She thought wistfully at times that, dirty or not, the city must be exciting. She glanced down at her ankle. Once when Nicholas had gone to the city with other *vaqueros,* he had brought back a silver bracelet for her ankle. She wore it every day, enjoying the way it shone in the sunlight, the way it slipped around her ankle when she and the other Indians on the rancho danced to the music of the *vaquero's* guitars in the evening when the day's work was done.

Calling her oldest son from outdoors, Juanita handed him a large kettle and told him to take it to the well and fill it with water. The roundup would begin as soon as the *vaqueros* began bringing in the wild horses. There was still much to be done.

An hour later, Juanita's employer galloped up to the front of the ranch house and, tying his horse to a hitching post, came inside the cool, thick-walled house. Mr. Shafter was coming, would be there in fifteen minutes, he announced.

Oscar Shafter was accompanied by an Indian guide when he rode his pony up to the ranch house. Both men rode Indian ponies. Shafter's was white and matched his white, wide-brimmed hat and white woolen coat. He had spurs of Mexican silver on his heels and wore buckskin pants like a real cowboy.

Walking in, he told of his adventures on the way.

He had stopped at the camp of the herdsman on the way in. The herdsman was a man who had been granted permission to graze cattle on part of Shafter's land. He

52

lived in a deep canyon with his wife and four daughters. It was dark and gloomy in the canyon but it was comfortable—there was a spring there that gave plenty of water for the family and the herds of sheep and cattle he kept.

Shafter had barely finished telling of his visit when the dogs that belonged to the *rancho* started barking and scampering around the corral.

"That means the *vaqueros* are coming with the mustangs already," Mr. Upton explained. "The dogs are excited. We'll have to tie them up when the branding begins."

Sounds of *"Hupa!"* and *"Anda!"* were heard from behind the house, along with the thunder of many hoofs. The visitor and his host ate quickly and went on out to the corral to perch on the top rail of the wooden fence. Oscar Shafter was having a new experience. He had never seen a wild horse roundup before.

At that time there were four hundred wild horses pastured on the Point Reyes peninsula. These wild horses did not belong to the Shafter family, they belonged to a group of men who, every year, brought them into the Point Reyes *rancho* to be branded. Three of the *vaqueros* who worked for the *rancho* were hired to bring in and brand the horses, and one of these cowboys was Nicolas, Juanita's husband.

The horses were driven, one hundred at a time, into the corral. When they were all inside, snorting and pawing the ground, the *vaqueros* began the real work of the day.

"Hi-yup! Hi-yup!" called Nicolas, and swung his *reata*, or lariat, around his head so swiftly that it whistled. He drove his pony close to one of the fiery-nostrilled mustangs. As the wild horse reared, his hoofs high in the air, Nicolas' *reata* flew through the air and the rope dropped around the colt's neck. Meantime one of the other *vaqueros* caught the colt's heels with his *reata,* and the two workers drew the ropes taut and threw the colt to the ground. Other ranch workers heated the branding iron and burned the owners' mark into the horse's hide.

The roundup watched by Oscar Shafter took place on a September day in 1858, eight years after California was admitted to the union of American states. Other roundups or rodeos were held each year to brand the cattle that roamed over the grassier parts of the peninsula, but these were usually held in the spring. During the hundreds of years when the Miwok Indians, ancestors of Nicolas and Juanita, had had their villages beside Drake's *Estero* and along the more sheltered parts of the peninsula coast, there were no cattle, either wild or tame. Nor horses. The Mission padres had introduced cows and horses to the area when they came up from the South and had taught the Indians to breed and care for them.

The horses brought to California were small and were known as Indian or Mexican ponies. The cattle were mostly longhorns like the ones later known as Texas longhorns. The cattle, too, came from Mexico. After the priests lost their mission properties, some of the cattle and horses went wild, roaming the countryside. Because of the need for horses both for travel and work on the ranches, there was great demand for tamed wild horses. That was why the wild mustangs were caught and branded, each year. Wild cattle were also useful but more dangerous. Anyone traveling on the Point Reyes peninsula was careful not to travel on foot.

The cattle on the peninsula ranches were raised chiefly for food, although other animal products were also important to the income of the ranchers. Animal fat was melted down to make tallow for candles, the only source of light in those early ranch days. Tallow was also used for soap-making—each *rancho* made its own soap. The hides of the cattle were cured and sold in the San Francisco markets, for the making of shoes and other leather garments.

The Shafters, Oscar and his brother, James Macmillan Shafter, had purchased the land on the Point Reyes peninsula early in the same year Oscar watched the wild horse roundup. And except for 2200 acres sold to Solomon Pierce, and the land around the headland that was sold to the United States government for a future lighthouse, the Shafters continued to own most of the peninsula for many years. In 1869, however, they divided the

land into six parcels, leasing most of the parcels for dairy farming. The city of San Francisco across the bay was growing, and its population needed milk, butter, and eggs. There was money to be made in the dairy business.

THE RED ELK GO AND
THE LIGHTHOUSE
COMES

SUNDAYS IN THE RANCH COUNTRY of the Point Reyes peninsula were times when the cowboys and other ranch hands were less busy than on weekdays. In the late 1800's, some of the cowboys used this spare time to tease the herds of Roosevelt elk that lived on the peninsula, galloping straight into the middle of a herd and scattering it, with no other purpose than to torment the animals. One spring a rancher who lived near the head of Tomales Bay saw a sight that his eyes told him could not be true, but it was. Dozens upon dozens of elk, the antlers of the males thrust high above the gray water, their female companions swimming beside them, were crossing Tomales Bay from the Point Reyes Peninsula to the northern mainland.

The crossing of the bay by the elk went on for weeks. There seemed to be no end to the stream of animals pouring down from Inverness Ridge toward the water. Sometimes one of the *vaqueros,* seeing the disappearing game, lifted his rifle and took aim at the moving beasts. Occasionally a shot hit its mark and the waters of the bay became crimson at the spot. But since it was obvious that any game killed in the water would be nearly impossible to bring home, there were only a few men foolish enough to waste their ammunition.

"What do you suppose started them?" one rancher would ask of a neighbor. All of the ranchers had enjoyed many an elk hunt in the past and felt dismayed by what they saw.

The general opinion was that the elk were tired of being tormented by the cowboys. They were heading for some place where the odds were better for them. Most of the ranchers were sure that all the elk would leave.

The exodus of the Roosevelt elk from the Point Reyes peninsula supposedly took place in the 1860's. There is no one still alive who was witness to the dramatic escape of the large red deer that once provided food and hides for the Miwok Indians. The story of the swim across the bay has become a legend, but it is no legend that the deer once lived at Point Reyes and that they disappeared northward about a hundred years ago and have never returned.

The disappearance of the Roosevelt elk was one of many happenings on the Point Reyes peninsula in the late 1800's, some happy, but many tragic.

On the morning of May 4, 1861, a very heavy fog lay

over the coast of the Point Reyes Beach. At the ranch nearest to the dangerous shoreline, *vaqueros* were preparing to go out and round up stray cattle that might have wandered too far from home during the dark night and early morning. Through the thick mist, the cowboys called to each other as they mounted their ponies and went galloping off into the gloom.

Two of the men headed towards the ocean, peering ahead of them for the shape of an animal, listening for the mournful bellowing of a hungry calf unable to find its mother. As they galloped along the trail in the direction of the ocean, one of them suddenly pulled hard on his horse's reins and asked, "Did you hear a cry for help?"

His companion also stopped his horse, and the two men paused on the edge of a bluff, staring in the direction of the ocean. Nothing was visible in the thick fog.

The shout for help came again, this time more distinctly. The second man said, "I've never heard of a talking cow, much less one that can yell for help. That was a human being. Somebody's in trouble down below."

The two cowboys dug their spurs into their horses and rode furiously down toward the ocean's sandy shore. They cut across the pastures that stretched above the sandstone cliffs.

"It's a clipper ship!" one of cowboys exclaimed when they reached the beach. "She's gone aground. Must be a fool of a captain, to ride in so close to this shore. There are a hundred rocks out there he could smash against; you'd think any seafaring man would know that much."

The two did not stand and talk about it long. Carleton Abbott, the other cowboy, dug his spurs into his horse and galloped along the beach. There were men in the water out there trying to make it to shore. He could not stand by and let men drown, fools or not.

The two cowboys rode as close to the crashing waves as they could, calling out to the ship and the men who were floundering in the water near the ship not to give up.

Several other ranch people had heard the cries for help by then and had begun to gather on the beach. One of the spectators shook his head as he stared out toward the ship and the swimming men. "They'll never make it in that kind of surf," he said.

Carleton Abbott meanwhile had been riding up and down the shore, studying the situation. After a few minutes, he rode back to the other men with an idea.

Following his instructions, the other horsemen let Abbott unwind their lariats from the horns of their saddles. He knotted all these together and tied one end of this long rope around his waist. Then he handed his fellow cowboys the other end of the tied-together lariats.

He took his own *reata* from his saddle horn and plunged into the waters, walking as far into the ocean as possible. When he could remain standing no longer, he twirled his rope in mid-air and sent it out over the head of one of the sailors floundering in the water. In a few minutes, the man had been dragged onto shore, where the waiting watchers had built a driftwood fire, and was drawn close to the heat to dry out. One by one, all but one of the men who had been aboard the *Sea Nymph* were saved by Abbott and his skillful *reata*. The one unlucky man was a steward who drowned before he could be rescued.

The *Sea Nymph* had wandered into a pocket of the ten-mile-long Point Reyes Beach in the thick fog. The navigator had been trying to pilot the ship by dead reckoning—without observing the stars, moon, or sun, because the fog was too thick for the sky to be seen. The danger of sailing so close to this shore were well known, but the pilot of the *Sea Nymph* had not realized how close the ship was to land. Thanks to the men from the ranches, the cargo of the *Sea Nymph* also was saved.

The *Sea Nymph* was the first wreck to be recorded on the main beach of the peninsula, but it was not to be the last. Between 1861 and 1934, twelve other ships came to grief in the same area.

Shipwrecks were common on other beaches of Point Reyes peninsula, too. In Drake's Bay, many ships followed the *San Agustín's* disastrous example, cracking to pieces in storms offshore. One ship came to ruin on the edge of Drake's *Estero*. This was owned by a colorful French-Mexican trader named Jose Yves Limantour. The wreck occurred in 1841. Limantour later became a notorious land speculator in San Francisco, but his name, although not highly regarded in California history, became immortalized through the shipwreck. The sand spit at the edge of Drake's *Estero* where the ship cracked is called Limantour Spit.

The recurring disasters around Point Reyes—many occurred right at the place where the headland thrusts into the Pacific—made California members of Congress agitate for a lighthouse to be erected on the headland. An appropriation for such construction was made as early as 1852, but nothing was done at that time. In the eastern part of the country, during the 1860s, attention was concentrated on the Civil War and the question of slavery. Shipwrecks on the Pacific Coast seemed of limited importance as the country split apart and fought.

When the Civil War came to an end, the country began to try to rebuild itself. The job had scarcely begun before Abraham Lincoln was assassinated. This event rocked the country and slowed down the reconstruction of the nation. The matter of a lighthouse on a rocky headland across from San Francisco received little attention for a number of years.

Finally, in 1870, nine years after the outbreak of the Civil War, a lighthouse was built on the western tip of the peninsula. On the first of December, it began flashing its warning from the bold, dark, dangerous headland. From a forty foot tower of forged iron plate, the revolving lens of the light steered ships and the men who sailed on them through driving wind, enormous seas, or soft, dense blankets of fog, around the point of land.

The light, weighing three tons and consisting of 1,000

pieces of glass, was made in Paris. It came around Cape Horn in a sailing ship and was brought by oxcart from the dock to the Point. The light flashed its signal, by means of revolving lenses, every five seconds. Its gleam could be seen more than twenty-five miles out at sea.

When the light was first established at Point Reyes, it was fueled with refined lard. The four wick oil lamp burned sixteen pints of this oil every ten hours. The lamp was lit at sunset and kept burning until sunrise every day of the year.

The keepers of the light, who lived in a two-story house above the lighthouse, often had to make their way down the steep slope through heavy winds, winds strong enough to blow them into the ocean. Fuel and supplies for the light were usually sent down from the summit of the headland by chute, but the keepers and the assistants, who took turns watching the light, had to take their chances with the great storms. When steps were built, a guard rail was constructed alongside to help the men keep their footing.

Today, the light at Point Reyes comes from a one thousand watt bulb, but because of the reflecting lenses it sends a 1,000,000 candlepower beam out across the darkness. The lens through which the light shines is the same lens brought around Cape Horn in 1870. Week-long fogs and gales of seventy-five to one hundred miles per hour still occur regularly at Point Reyes and the Coast Guard Station men who have replaced the "keepers of the light" of early days, keep a close watch on the seas around the Point. Today there is also a great, booming two-tone foghorn whose "blast and grunt" warns ships away from the headland.

WHEN THE
EARTH CRACKED

SHIPWRECKS CONTINUED TO HAPPEN around Point Reyes despite the lighthouse and the foghorn. Five years after the lighthouse was built, a rancher walking along the shore of Point Reyes' long coastline, saw a ghostly ship lying offshore, apparently caught on the rocks. Through the thick fog, it reminded the rancher of legends of ghost ships that wander the seas of the world, and for a few moments he felt an odd chill. He went to notify other ranchers, returning with them to discuss what to do about the lonely-looking ship that showed no signs of human life aboard it.

"I think I can swim out there," one of the ranchers said. "I'll go out and try to rouse somebody, if they're not all dead. The fog is going. They could get the ship off the rocks and be on their way, unless there's a hole in her." Without waiting for anyone else, the rancher struck out into the water, disappearing from his friends' view in a little while.

When the swimmer had been gone quite a while, the other ranchers became alarmed and started discussing what to do. But then one of them caught sight of him.

The rancher who had gone out to the ship came wading out of the shallow water near shore a few minutes later.

"There's no one on board the ship and what's more, there aren't even any ship's papers to say whose vessel she is."

The men looked at each other, thoroughly puzzled. Even if everyone on the ship had jumped overboard and been lost in the sea, the ship's papers should have been left behind.

It was a mystery. The ranchers, unable to solve it, returned to their homes. Three days later word came from San Francisco that the wrecked ship was the *Warrior Queen* and that the men who had sailed her had made their way to San Francisco in three small boats, taking the ship's papers with them. The *Warrior Queen* smashed herself to pieces on the rocky shore, but one of the ranchers salvaged a souvenir. For many years the wooden figurehead of a fighting queen was on display at his ranch.

A peace similar to the time when the Indians lived on the peninsula existed in the late 1800s and early 1900s on the peninsula ranches. The occasional wrecks of ships along the shore, like that of the *Warrior Queen,* provided excitement, but most of the ranchers' days were spent in hard work and a quiet life. Although some of the ranchers raised beef cattle as in the early days of the *ranchos,* most of them were dairymen. They milked their cows by hand, made their own butter and cheese, and hauled their products by oxcart to the schooner landing on the main arm of Drake's *Estero,* as it was formally called. There the dairy products were loaded onto small schooners and sailed across the Bay of San Francisco to the city markets. The arm of the *estero* where these schooners landed is still called Schooner Bay, although no boats that large dock there now.

The soil and climate of the ranching portion of the peninsula was good for cattle. Grazing plants such as filaree, bunch and foxtail grass, and clover grew there naturally or were planted. Springs of fresh water were available to every ranch.

Between the gold rush years and the silver rush years, and during the time of the Civil War, the Point Reyes

farmers were particularly prosperous. A few feeble attempts at finding gold and silver on the peninsula were quickly abandoned, but the mineral riches from the Comstock and Mother Lode mines found their way into the pockets of the ranchers, eventually. Miners and speculators needed food, and the ranches of Marin County became a food basket for the city across the bay that had grown up around the California gold rush.

High above the Pacific, on the point now called Tomales Point, the Pierce family, descendants of the Solomon Pierce who had first bought land from the Shafters, was among the foremost of the prosperous dairymen. The house and outbuildings on the Pierce ranch, like those of the other ranches, were lighted by fuel oil lamps, and the men rode horses or drove wagons to the neighboring towns and to the county seat, San Rafael.

Descendants of the Miwok worked on the ranches, some intermarrying with descendants of the Spaniards

and other white men. For many years, white men and Indians lived together in the area, with peace and prosperity for the white men, and acceptance on the part of the Indians.

Like the early Indians, the ranchers hunted wild game, although it was not essential to their existence. Their hunting was for sport. Among these hunters, Timoteo Murphy was famous, riding through the grass and timber of the Point Reyes peninsula, gun in hand, often an Indian cowboy beside him. The elk had gone, but the smaller deer remained; and there were bobcats and gray foxes, rabbits by the hundreds, ducks, and other game birds.

Hunting became so popular on the peninsula that around 1890, twenty years after the building of the lighthouse, a group of wealthy Californians leased land from the ranchers near Olema, a village at the edge of Bear Valley. These hunters opened the Olema Country Club and hired as the first keeper of the lodge Jean Garcia, son of that Rafael Garcia who had once, as a soldier, defended the San Rafael mission.

People from all over the world came to the Olema Club when it was at its most flourishing. Among them was Ignace Paderewski, world-famous pianist.

For those whose interest lay in other directions, there were marshes and woods where wild berries were abundant—service berries, red elderberry, huckleberry. The meadows sounded with the music of tule wrens, goldfinches, warblers, and other land birds. On the beaches, sandpipers and curlews skittered across the sand, leaving the geometry of their imprints on the wet sand, until the water washed them away.

The peace of Point Reyes, when it was shattered, was shattered not by man, but by nature. Pale light was spreading over the 80,000 acres of land belonging to the Shafter families one morning in 1906. Through the open window of her bedroom, a little girl was awakened by the sound of birds in a buckeye tree near her home. She yawned sleepily, thinking that when she was up and dressed and had eaten breakfast, she might climb to the nest of moss she had made high in the tree. It was a wonderful place to hide from her father, who expected her to take the place of the son he had never had and was always telling her to help with the horses and other animals. Mary Shafter, granddaughter of the two brothers who had, in 1858, bought most of the Point Reyes peninsula, turned over and went back to sleep. It was barely five o'clock in the morning.

Ten minutes later Mary, like hundreds of other men, women, and children living along Tomales Bay, was jolted awake by being thrown out of bed onto the floor. Dazed, she lay there a few minutes while the world rocked back and forth under her.

The rocking finally stopped. Mary scrambled to her feet and began to run in her long nightdress to her grandmother's room. She had barely reached the hall between the bedrooms however when another jolt threw her to

71

the floor again. She began to cry, thinking that everyone in the house must have died, but a few seconds later she heard her father, Payne Shafter, shout, "The world has come to an end! Where's my Bible?"

Papa couldn't be dead, to yell like that, Mary thought, drying her tears. He was in Grandma's room, from the sound of his voice. She crept along in the same direction, afraid to stand up and walk. Above her she heard a whir of wings. Looking up fearfully, she saw her grandmother's canaries fly in through the open door of the old lady's bedroom. Mary stood up then and went to her grandmother. Her father, and her sister Helen, were already there. Her mother was not at home.

"Preep! Preep!" cried the canaries. Mary's father had caught them and was holding a bird in each hand.

"What's happened?" Mary asked, but before anyone could answer, plaster from the wall beside her fell to the floor and plaster dust flew up, choking her. She closed her eyes to keep out the dust and heard a raucous voice yell, "Ha! Ha! Isn't it awful? Isn't it awful?"

The parrot had escaped from his cage, too!

Mary's grandmother, who had climbed back into her bed when the plaster fell, told Mary's father to put all the birds back into their cages. "It was an earthquake," she declared, "but it's probably over."

Mumbling passages from the Book of Revelation, Mary's father reluctantly started back toward the room where the canary cage was kept. He had reached the kitchen and was starting for the dining room when

Addie, the cook, came past him with a lighted lamp in her hand. Seeing her master looking wild and holding canaries in his hand, the cook became even more frightened than she already was and flung the lamp out of the nearest window. The flames blew backward and the heat struck Mr. Shafter's face. He took this for a further sign from Heaven. Letting the canaries go, he shouted, "Get down on your knees, all of you! It's come! The end of the world is here!" As he spoke, he dropped to his own knees.

April 18, 1906, was the day that the famous earthquake nearly destroyed San Francisco. Two quakes followed one on top of each other within a minute of time. Somewhere far below the earth's surface the rocks and earth shifted along a 270 mile line. Boiling upward, the gigantic upheaval broke the upper earth apart.

A geological fault is a fracturing of the earth's surface. The San Andreas fault, which runs along Tomales Bay and separates the Point Reyes peninsula from the mainland, is one of the greatest fractures on the entire planet. Movements deep in the earth sometimes shift one edge of such a fracture in one direction and the other edge in another. This was what happened on that April morning in the San Francisco Bay region. The most severe shift of the fault occurred in northern Marin County and in Sonoma County directly north of it.

At the same time that Mary Shafter was sleepily planning to climb her favorite tree, the narrow gauge train that ran through the town of Olema and on to the neighboring town of Point Reyes Station was starting out on its day's journey. There was no one waiting in the railroad station at that early hour, but the conductor sang out his "All aboard!" as he did every other morning. He swung himself onto the coach and prepared to yank the cord that would tell the engineer to move the train. As the conductor's hand reached for the cord, the train and its locomotive turned over on its side. The three-man crew jumped off as it fell. None were injured.

A schoolteacher who lived on Tomales Bay, jolted awake by the shock, went to her window to see what had happened. She watched in speechless astonishment as a ten foot wave built itself up on the waters of the bay and rolled toward her. Not far away, a two-story hotel and the stables that belonged to it leaned sidewise and slid into the water.

The disasters that resulted from the earthquake were varied. Some people went temporarily out of their minds. Cattle on ranches were thrown to the ground, brick chimneys crumbled, and water tanks toppled. Railway tracks buckled and broke, some jerked completely out of line.

A cow is supposed to have fallen into a wide crack that opened up on the Bear Valley Ranch, where the Shafter family home was, but this story has never been proved. The persons who claimed to have seen the cow disappear into the crack said that the crack closed again and swallowed up the cow, leaving only her hind hoofs and tail showing. By the time another witness arrived at the corral to check the story, the hoofs and tail had also disappeared.

Whether or not a cow disappeared in a fissure, many other strange events did happen. On Inverness Ridge, which divides the peninsula, a small lake, in the middle of a forest of Douglas firs known as the Black Forest, had all the water drained from it at the time of the earthquake. Now the water has returned and the area is called Mud Lake.

THE PLATE OF BRASSE

IT WAS A WARM SUMMER DAY in 1936. Beryl Shinn of San Francisco and a companion were making their first visit to the hills, streams, and beaches of Marin County. The two were driving along one of the main roads leading from San Rafael toward the towns of Sausalito and Mill Valley. They had decided to turn off the main road soon and explore one of the smaller roads—and perhaps find a good place to eat their picnic lunch.

Shinn drove at a moderate pace along the highway glancing occasionally at the town of Greenbrae immediately to their right. He worked in a department store in the city. Weekends were his only chance to get into the country, but he had barely begun to look for a country road when his car began to wobble and he had difficulty controlling it. It was his bad tire. He steered the car off the highway onto a shoulder of land.

76

The two friends climbed out of the car after it stopped and looked at the tire. "We'll have to take the thing off and patch it," Shinn said, "but let's relax first." He glanced around at the tidal estuary some distance away, and at the grim walls of the state prison at Point San Quentin, then up at the bluff rising high above where they stood. "How about climbing up there and looking for a place to sit and eat? There ought to be a great view up there."

His companion looked up at the bluff, too. "I'm willing to try the climb if you are."

The two young men scrambled and clawed their way up the bluff, dodging under a fence of barbed wire and finally reaching the top. The soil at the top was rocky, and the young men began throwing stones over the edge of the bluff for sport. Discovering that even the larger rocks could have pieces broken off them, they threw parts of them, too. It was good exercise, and they enjoyed themselves. But then Shinn saw something sticking out from under one of the rocks. He tugged at the object and got it loose. It was a metal plate about one eighth of an inch thick, five inches wide, and eight inches long.

Shinn didn't know what it was, but he decided he could use it to patch up a hole in the floor of his car. It seemed to be made of iron. He thrust it toward his companion, who agreed that the plate would work out fine for Shinn's car.

After the friends had finished their picnic, they returned to Shinn's car, taking the metal plate with them.

Shinn tossed it into the trunk of the car and got busy repairing his punctured tire so they could return to San Francisco.

Beryl Shinn put the metal plate out of his mind for about a month until, one pleasant day, he decided to try to repair the hole in his car. He got the plate out and for the first time noticed that there was an inscription on it. Curious, he took it into his house and scrubbed it with soap, water, and a brush. There were definitely some characters or letters on the plate. Now quite interested, Shinn called up some of his friends and asked them to come over and have a look, to see if any of them could read the inscription, because he couldn't. The friend who had been with him when he found the plate decided that the word at the end of the signature looked like DRAKE. He thought the piece of metal could be important. The letters weren't modern day English letters. As a student of Dr. Herbert Bolton at Berkeley, he suggested that Shinn get in touch with a historian and ask what he thought it was. Dr. Bolton might even be a good choice since he was an expert on West Coast history.

Shinn said he would think about it, but he put the plate away for the time being. He felt timid about approaching a man like Dr. Bolton with an object found on a hillside. If it was valuable, he told himself, it would have been discovered a long time before. It couldn't possibly be anything important. But finally, after about six months and much talk about the metal plate with his friends, Beryl Shinn telephoned Dr. Bolton.

"Describe it carefully," the historian said. "Tell me every detail."

So Shinn described the plate, mentioning finally that there was a round hole in the left-hand corner and that after he had scrubbed the metal, it hadn't looked quite so dark in color. "I realize now that it isn't iron," Shinn said.

Dr. Bolton was one of many historians who had studied the question of where the famous English sea captain, Sir Francis Drake, had careened his ship, the *Golden Hinde*, in 1579. To careen a ship means to haul it onto dry ground in order to make repairs; the chaplain of Drake's ship, a man named Fletcher, had kept a journal of Drake's voyage in which the chaplain had described the place where this careening took place. Fletcher had reported that before Drake set out again upon his journey, after the ship was made seaworthy, he had taken possession of the bay where he rested and its surrounding lands in the name of Queen Elizabeth of England. Drake had ordered a "plate of brasse" to be made, with a hole the size of a coin on which the Queen's face was imprinted to be left in one corner, so that the sovereign's image would be on the brass plate. According to Fletcher's account, the brass plate was attached to a strong post and left as evidence of the possession of the area by England.

Dr. Bolton was excited about Shinn's find, thinking it

likely that Shinn had found the brass plate. He asked Shinn to bring the plate to him and promised that a thorough study would be made to test its authenticity. Experts in history and metallurgy were then consulted and, in 1937, the California Historical Society announced that it was indeed the Drake plate that had been found in Marin County on the shore of San Francisco Bay. This proved, said the Society, that the famous captain had landed somewhere on San Francisco Bay and had probably discovered that port years before later explorers did.

When the story was published in the San Francisco newspapers, however, William Caldeira, chauffeur to a Mr. Leon Bocqueraz of San Francisco, announced that he had found the plate three years before Shinn found it, but not near San Francisco Bay. Mr. Caldeira said he had found the plate of brass near a road on the Laguna Ranch close to Drake's Bay. He had showed it to his employer, but Mr. Bocqueraz, who had been hunting all day, was tired and not interested.

"It's probably off some ship," he said. "Things like that wash ashore here all the time."

Laguna Ranch is one of the ranches on the Point Reyes peninsula. The place where Caldeira found the plate was approximately a mile and a half inland from Drake's Bay. The chauffeur said he had carried the plate around in his employer's car for a time but had eventually thrown it out somewhere near the spot where Shinn had found it.

This threw historians into a new flurry of argument. Did Drake careen his ship on the shores of San Francisco Bay, or did he do so on the shores of Drake's Bay on the Marin coast?

The question remains unsettled, although most experts believe that Drake landed somewhere on the Marin coast, very probably at Drake's Bay. His chaplain's description of the light-colored bluffs past which the *Golden Hinde* sailed, fits the bluffs at the small bay that George Vancouver, Drake's fellow countryman, named after the famous sea captain in 1790. Whether the Elizabethan explorer discovered the bay or not, it bears his name. In 1854, the United States Coast Survey referred to it as Drake's Bay, thus putting an official stamp on the name.

As for the famous plate of brass, it belongs to the University of California at Berkeley and can be seen at Ban-

BEE IT KNOWNE VNTO ALL MEN BY THESE PRESENTS JVNE. 17. 1579, BY THE GRACE OF GOD AND IN THE NAME OF HERR MAJESTY QVEEN ELIZABETH. OF ENGLAND AND HERR SVCCESSORS FOREVER, I TAKE POSSESSION OF THIS KINGDOME WHOSE KING AND PEOPLE. FREELY RESIGNE THEIR RIGHT AND TITLE IN THE WHOLE LAND VNTO HERR MAIESTIES KEEPEING NOW NAMED BY ME AN TO BEE KNOWNE VNTO ALL MEN AS NOVA ALBION. FRANCIS DRAKE.

croft Historical Library, in a glass-enclosed case. The inscription on the plate reads:

BEE IT KNOWNE UNTO ALL MEN BY THESE PRESENTS
June 17 1579
BY THE GRACE OF GOD AND IN THE NAME OF HER MAJESTY
QUEEN ELIZABETH OF ENGLAND AND HER SUCCESSORS
FOREVER I TAKE POSSESSION OF THIS KINGDOM WHOSE
KING AND PEOPLE FREELY RESIGNE THEIR RIGHT AND
TITLE IN THE WHOLE LAND UNTO HER MAJESTIES
KEEPEING NOW NAMED BY MEE AND TO BE KNOWNE UNTO
ALL MEN AS NOVA ALBION

FRANCIS DRAKE

And in one corner was a hole for an English sixpence.

The wooden post to which the brass plate was attached would long ago have rotted away. But it may be that the stones of the fort Drake and his men are supposed to have built, at the place where they landed, may yet be found and prove forever where he brought the *Golden Hinde* ashore.

One year after the Drake plate was found by Beryl Shinn and while historians were still arguing about it, something else was happening to Marin county and San Francisco. A man named Joseph Strauss had planned and had hired hundreds of men to build a suspension bridge over the Golden Gate, the entrance to San Francisco Bay. The Golden Gate Bridge, as it is called, joining San Francisco and Marin County, was opened to

82

the public on May 27, 1937. Thousands of people walked across it on opening day, using the walkways along the sides of the bridge. The rose-orange towers of Mr. Strauss' bridge are familiar to people from all parts of the United States; those who have not seen them in actuality have seen pictures. Since that day in May, millions of cars have streamed across the bridge to enjoy the scenery and sunshine of Marin County. Not many, however, had a chance to visit the wild beaches of the Point Reyes peninsula, at the time the bridge was first in use. The roads there were rough, and the beaches belonged to ranchers and could be used only with their permission. The wind and the surf, the pelicans, cormorants and gulls, the bobcats and gray foxes, remained pretty much undisturbed except for the ranchers themselves and a few abalone hunters and clam diggers.

Opposite the Point Reyes Seashore across Tomales bay lies the tiny town of Marshall, California. Overlooking bay and town is an imposing building that was once the headquarters of the Marconi wireless receiving station. The building, and those surrounding it, now belong to the Synanon Foundation, which operates a rehabilitation center for former drug addicts. Until Synanon bought the buildings, they had been vacant since 1930 when the Marconi receiving station moved to the Point Reyes peninsula, establishing itself in a forest of towers on the ocean's edge. These towers are the property of the Radio Communications Association of America, known as RCA.

RCA is a telegraph "point-to-point" receiving station —this means, actually, country to country. It sends no messages, only receives them, but in nearby Bolinas, California, RCA has a transmitting station also. The Point Reyes station, in 1934, received the fourth cable ever to come across the Pacific—it came from Tokyo, a distance of 5100 miles.

Next door to RCA is another kind of receiving station belonging to the American Telephone and Telegraph Company. This station handles only trans-Pacific telephone messages, no telegrams. It has been on the peninsula since the late 1930s to receive calls from other countries. AT&T also handles high seas messages. If someone on board a ship on the high seas needs to get a telephone call through to someone on the West Coast of the United States, the call goes through AT&T's peninsula receivers.

These receivers may not always remain on the Point Reyes peninsula, but they are part of its history.

BATTLE FOR
THE SEASHORE

THE FAMILY OF FOUR in the station wagon had followed the road marked Sir Francis Drake Boulevard from the city of San Rafael to Inverness at the edge of the Point Reyes peninsula. Strangers to the area, they were on their first trip to California. Neither of the two boys in the car had ever been close to an ocean. They were impatiently awaiting its appearance.

"You'll have to make do with the bay for a little while," the boys' father told them, waving his hand at Tomales Bay. The bay was on the right-hand side of the road they traveled. Across it could be seen the town of Marshall.

"A bay's not as good as an ocean," complained the oldest boy.

The father pushed down more heavily on the accelerator. It was the middle of the afternoon. If they were to reach the beach before the sun left it, they would have to hurry.

"There's the road!" one of the boys exclaimed. "Look! It says Drake's Bay. That's where the man at the filling station said there was a public beach."

The father slowed the car and made a left turn in the direction the sign indicated. It was a good road and seemed quite new. He wondered, briefly, that it should be in so much better condition than the county highway on which they had been driving. But he kept going and after a few miles came to the crest of a hill, from which he could see a road descending toward the ocean.

"Not far now," he said.

His wife smiled. "I'll unpack the lunch when we get there, and you and the boys can beachcomb." The family was planning to broil hamburgers over a beach fire, something the boys had never had an opportunity to do before. They were from Nebraska, far from any ocean.

The station wagon descended the hill. A fence at the bottom bore a sign which said NO TRESPASSING.

"That's funny," said the children's mother. "We were told it was a county beach, open to everyone. Dad, go ask that man coming toward us if this is Drake's Bay."

"All right." The father got out of his car and walked toward the stranger. "How do we get to the beach, can you tell me?"

"You go back the way you came, over that hill, and keep on the highway for about ten more miles," the man said. "The beach is right down that way." He pointed vaguely north. "But you can't reach it from here."

Dismayed, the father said, "It's too late to go all that way back and then ten more miles. We have to get back to the city. Can't we picnic here, down by the water?" He looked unhappily at the NO TRESPASSING sign.

"No, sir, you can't," the man answered unsmilingly. "This is private property."

"But the sign on the highway pointed this way for Drake's Bay."

"Drake's Bay is quite large. This is part of it, but it's not the public beach," the man said. He turned away, going toward a building under construction.

Gloomily, the family from Nebraska retraced their way to the highway and continued on it until they finally reached the public beach.

The road that the visiting midwesterners had accidentally turned onto was a road built by a firm of developers who had bought up over a thousand acres of the Point Reyes peninsula beach area for a subdivision. The purchase was made soon after steps had been taken in Washington for the government to acquire the peninsula for a national seashore park. The proposal that this be done was not a new one. Those who loved the California seacoast and had seen Point Reyes had long advocated such a move. But not everyone was in accord with the idea. Knowing that they must move fast, the developers who wanted to replace beauty with profit brought bulldozers, power shovels, and roadscrapers into the heart of the proposed national park, while it was still in private hands. Their plan was to create a subdivision to be called Drake's Beach Estates, utilizing one of the most beautiful areas on the peninsula. If their plans had been completed, only a few people, wealthy enough to own oceanfront property, would ever have had a chance to see Limantour Spit or know its wildlife, Indian mounds, and beaches. *No Trespassing* signs would have replaced native shrubbery.

Only a few of the developers' proposed homes were actually built before action was taken to stop them, but there was to be a long battle between the farsighted men and women who wanted to preserve the peninsula for everyone and those individuals who wanted to exploit it for their own profit.

The story of how the peninsula of Point Reyes became a national seashore began while Franklin D. Roosevelt was President of the United States. In 1935, Conrad Wirth, who later became the director of the National Parks Service, surveyed the peninsula and recommended that 53,000 acres of it be set aside for future recreational use. At that time the land was worth less than fifty dollars an acre.

Wirth's recommendation lay in the files of the National Parks Service for over twenty years. There was no money to buy the land on Point Reyes, and not much interest in Congress in having a national seashore park, particularly one on the West Coast.

Then, in 1957, a group of citizens who had watched the fast-disappearing shoreline land on both coasts falling into the hands of developers, raised money to make a study of the lands that might still be available on the Pacific Coast. That study, made by the Parks Service, declared that the Point Reyes peninsula was the most promising of all available Pacific coastline land for a national park.

Release of that study kicked off the battle for the seashore. Many people put in time, energy, and money to make the Point Reyes National Seashore a reality, too many to name. But perhaps the one deserving the most credit was former Congressman Clement Woodnut Miller of California, in whose Congressional district the Point Reyes peninsula lay.

Miller, generally called "Clem" by those who knew him, grew up in Wilmington, Delaware. His love for the outdoors and natural beauty began early in his life, thanks to his mother who took him on expeditions into the countryside and taught him to recognize and name many flowers and trees and birds. When Clem was old enough, he joined a Boy Scout troop and became an Eagle Scout. His hikes with the Scouts and his camping expeditions, deepened his love for and his knowledge of, natural things.

As he grew up, Clem was influenced strongly by other personalities, particularly his Uncle Tom. Uncle Tom, Clem's father's brother, was deeply involved in Nevada politics during the years Clem was becoming an adult.

On visits to the West, Clem went with his uncle on long drives around the country, becoming more and more excited by the wild western landscape he saw, and the openness of the land, where one could drive for hundreds of miles without finding many people.

"I'm going to live in the West when I grow up," he told his uncle one day when they stopped on the top of a Nevada mountain to look out over a beautiful valley spread below them.

Uncle Tom, who was very tall and had a great, booming laugh, took off his ten gallon hat and waved it at a red-tailed hawk that was wheeling above them in the sky.

"I sure hope you mean that, Clem," he said.

Clem Miller did mean it. When he was very small, he and his father and mother had lived for two years in San Francisco. Although he remembered only a few things about that time, he did remember seeing the Pacific Ocean and the rolling hills of the country around the city. And he remembered being happy in California. His visits to his uncle in Nevada served to deepen his feeling for the West.

The travels with his Uncle Tom also aroused another kind of interest in Clem Miller. Because his uncle was involved in Nevada politics, many of his uncle's friends were also people interested in political issues. The boy listened to the conversations between his uncle and the others and became more and more aware of how alive some of these individuals were. They cared intensely about what was happening in their state and in the nation, and they talked with both knowledge and enthusiasm. Young Clem began to see that taking an active part in political battles, fighting for what a person believed to be right, could be a stimulating and useful way to spend one's life. Politics was in his heritage. His grandfather Miller had been Governor of Delaware. Governor Miller, too, had loved the West—he helped to open up the state of Nevada to the railroads.

So, many years later, after Clem Miller graduated from college and served five years in the United States Army during World War II, at age thirty-one he kept his promise to himself and his uncle and moved West. He and his wife lived for a year in the famous ghost town of Virginia City, Nevada, and then moved to Marin County, California, where they remained until Miller was elected to Congress in 1960.

Even before he became a Congressman, Miller had worked for conservation projects. He was particularly interested in the beautiful, half-wild peninsula of Point Reyes. With his wife and daughters he spent many weekends in a cottage in the little town of Inverness. When weather permitted, the Millers spent those weekends outdoors. They climbed the hills and visited the wild beaches, enjoying the beauties of the flowering yellow bush lupine in spring and the crimson toyon berries in fall. The Point Reyes peninsula landscape became part of Clem Miller's life and imagination.

One day in 1958, before Miller was elected to Congress, he learned that the Marin County board of supervisors planned to pass a resolution at the next weekly meeting, a resolution opposing any attempt by the federal government to make a national park of Point Reyes. Clem Miller went to that meeting as a citizen to protest the proposed resolution and to ask the board to wait

before taking such a determined stand. His appearance was unscheduled and when he asked to speak, a member of the board said, "You are not on our agenda, Mr. Miller. I suggest you wait until a later meeting."

Clem Miller knew that to wait for a later meeting would be a mistake. The one woman on the board, Mrs. Vera Schultz, came to his rescue.

"I think we should let Mr. Miller have a few minutes," she said, "before we vote on the resolution. He is a citizen of our county, a working conservationist, and a property owner in the area adjoining the peninsula."

Grudgingly the chairman of the board permitted Clem Miller to ask for a delay on the resolution. Despite his plea, however, the four men on the board voted for the resolution. Mrs. Schultz voted against it, and this kept the subject open for further consideration.

Clem Miller's appearance before the Marin County board of supervisors was among the earliest efforts in the long, hard fight, in Congress and out, by the friends of conservation, to secure the peninsula for a national park.

After Miller was elected to the House of Representatives, he began working for the Seashore. Before he took his seat in the House, he met with experts of the National Parks Service to discuss the number of acres they believed would be necessary to create a good park at Point Reyes. They recommended the full 53,000 acres suggested by Conrad Wirth twenty years or more before. Miller was not in office six months when, together with two California Senators, Thomas Kuchel and Clair Engle, he pushed through a request for $15,000 to make a more thorough study of the peninsula. In July of that same year, Miller in the House and Engle in the Senate, introduced the first Point Reyes National Seashore authorization bill.

By then, the people of Marin County, and especially the people of that part of it which is the Point Reyes peninsula, were becoming very excited. Ranchers with dairy farms on the peninsula believed that their way of life was to be taken away from them. The Marin County supervisors began getting angry letters from property owners and on the other hand pleading letters from people who were determined to have the Seashore park. An organization called the Point Reyes National Seashore Foundation was founded. Professors of zoology and biology, anthropologists, ornithologists, PTA groups, Boy Scouts, and others lined up with those who wanted the Seashore. Ranchers, real estate people and property owners who wanted to develop the peninsula for subdivision, organized the opposition. The West Marin Property Owners' Association was formed to try to prevent the authorization of the national park.

On April 13, 1960, the Marin County supervisors played host to a visiting group of members of Congress. The county board by then had several new members, and the attitude toward the Seashore was much more favorable. Among the visiting congressmen was Clem Miller. The delegation from Washington was flown over the

Point Reyes peninsula in helicopters, so that they might see for themselves what it was that Congressman Miller and Senators Engel and Kuchel were trying to persuade them to appropriate money for.

The day was a sparkling, spectacular one. The sun shone down on the Pacific Ocean and the gleaming sand of the peninsula beaches. It sent millions of lights danc-

95

ing in the water and made the area seem almost Caribbean. The curling foam of the long lines of breakers north from the headland, the gulls wheeling and dipping at the water's edge, even the deer on the ridges were visible. One of the ranchers on the peninsula commented bitterly, "Those Congressmen had better remind themselves that the Lord was with them on Point Reyes that day. Almost any other day in that same week they would have found fog, and they wouldn't even have seen Point Reyes." A newspaperman representing the county newspaper, who was along on the flight, told his wife later, "It was all over as far as those Washington people were concerned, after that spectacularly beautiful flight. We're going to get the Seashore."

It was, however, a long way from being over. The following day a public hearing was held at the College of Marin in Kentfield, California. Individuals from both sides spoke. In opposition to the Seashore were ranchers and the lawyer for the West Marin Property Owners. A rancher, explaining that he was not an educated man, said, "I never went past the eighth grade in school. I milk cows." This was in response to a plea to the ranchers to think of the future of the peninsula as a park.

Congressman Clem Miller warned people that they had to make a choice. "Either we all have several cars and two or three television sets, or we cut down on these things to provide recreation for ourselves and our children."

A rancher answered, "I think we should think about

96

food. Do we want food on the tables of our country or shall we send the children out to play at dinnertime?" It was a bitter remark, made by a man who felt that all he had worked for in his lifetime was going to be taken away from him.

An elderly woman, owner of several ranches on the peninsula, was more moving. She had been born in Europe and had wanted to come to America from the time she was a child because, she said, she believed it to be a land where respect for human dignity could be found. "I thought it was the land of the free, of justice for all, a land that didn't let anyone get trampled on," she said. She went on to describe the early years on her ranch, when there were only mud roads and no electricity. With a mixture of tears and anger, she finished, "If my ranches were to be taken for defense of the country, well, you have to sacrifice for the benefit of all . . . But for recreation, what kind of recreation did I have when I was a youngster?"

One of the more surprising testimonies on the side of the Seashore was given by the wife of a lumberman. Lumbermen have often been enemies of conservation, but this woman's husband wanted Point Reyes to be protected by the government. He said that the lumber from the trees on the peninsula was not valuable, that it could not be successfully stored in lumber yards because the sun and heat caused it to warp, twist, and cup.

The lumberman's wife added her own comment, as a wife and mother: ". . . we have heard all about economics today. It is very difficult to measure the economic value of a redwood tree or a boy's first fish in a natural lake. My children were swimming in Tomales Bay on Tuesday of the past week—and it is only April. I can't agree with the gloomy picture of the Point Reyes climate that some have given here today."

A thirteen-year-old Boy Scout, William Stephenson of Mill Valley, Marin County, told of how a former Congressman, William Kent, had given Muir Woods with its tall, ancient redwoods to the people of the United States. "Mr. Kent saw not board feet, but God's handiwork in the beauty of those old trees," Bill Stephenson said. He added that he and his fellow Scouts had seen some giant redwoods six feet or more in diameter and over six hundred years old cut down. He had seen logging roads built, bulldozing and dragging done without concern for erosion, and once he and his friends had seen a stream that had been the spawning ground of salmon and steelhead muddied and clogged. The young Scout asked that this type of disaster not be permitted at Point Reyes.

The arguments continued. Clem Miller and others of the legislators believed that cows and ranches were a valid part of the pleasure to be found on Point Reyes. But Miller knew, too, that some of the ranchers were planning to quit farming. Small operation dairying was becoming less and less profitable. Although the ranchers pleaded for their "way of life," the day was not far off, Miller knew, when the ranch owners or their heirs would sell their land to developers and the beaches of Marin

County would be forever closed to the public.

Meantime, the Washington legislators worked out a formula that permitted the ranches that were to be purchased by the government for the Seashore to be leased back to the ranchers. Dairy and cattle ranching was to continue on the peninsula ranches as long as the owners wished, but no owner could break up his ranch into developments, either for homes or for commercial property.

The bill authorizing the federal government to purchase 53,000 acres of land on the Point Reyes peninsula for a National Seashore, passed both houses of Congress, was signed by President John F. Kennedy, and became law in September, 1962.

A month later, on a stormy night in October, 1962, while campaigning for re-election to Congress, Clem Miller, with pilot George Head and Head's thirteen-year-old son Ronald, flew north from Marin County in a private plane, heading for Crescent City, California. The plane crashed into a mountain near Eureka and all three persons in the plane were killed.

Clem Miller is buried at Point Reyes, the first citizen of the country ever to be buried in a national park. His knoll overlooks the white cliffs of Drake's Bay and the stormy, dramatic, beautiful Pacific Ocean the Congressman so deeply loved. Only a small plate marker graces the site, but flowers blow in the spring breezes on the hillside in Bear Valley, insects hum in the grass, and birds sing and nest nearby, making it the kind of resting place Clem Miller would have loved.

AS A
NATIONAL SEASHORE

IT WAS A WARM, BRIGHT DAY in September, with a low tide
due around three o'clock in the afternoon. A few young
men with surfboards were trying to find combers swift
enough to carry them into shore at Drake's Beach in the
Seashore park, about twenty-five miles from the Park
Service headquarters. Other groups picnicked on rocks
at the edge of the sea; some were eating sandwiches on
the picnic tables and benches in the shelter provided by
the Park Service when it took over what had once been
the county beach. The shelter, although new, had been
built with rustic-type materials and looked as though it
had grown handsomely out of the sand. Down at the
water's edge, sea gulls waited for the waves to bring in
food, ignoring the surfers and the picnickers. Occasionally one or two birds flew out low over the water, their
wing-shadows falling on the combers, but most of the

100

birds waited almost motionless on shore. Smaller birds also waited.

Two girls of college age drove a small car into the parking lot near the beach shelter and walked down to where a few sanderlings ran before the waves. The girls were barefoot and wearing shorts. They set out briskly, heading south toward the mouth of Drake's *Estero*, where long before, Sebastian Cermeño's galleon, the *San Agustín*, had been smashed to pieces in a storm. The receding tide had packed the sand hard and they were able to walk easily along the coast below the high, cream-colored bluffs. An occasional tide pool had formed inside flat tables of rock close to the bluffs and in the clear water, the girls saw barnacles and limpets clinging to the rock. Jellyfish sprawled like melted pudding on the sand, and sand crabs scuttled ahead of the girls' feet.

The college girls were headed for the mouth of the *estero*, to see for themselves the four-armed historic salt water inlet from the sea, a mile-and-a-half walk. Only at low tide is it possible to complete the walk without having to wade through considerable water; but when possible, the walk is worth making. Between the mouth of the *estero* and its upper end is a long sandbar. The bar is a resting place for shore and seabirds, and when the tide is low it appears to be covered with white foam. The whiteness comes from the resting gulls, some of whom are white or partially white, and also, in winter, from white pelicans. Because white pelicans fish for their food from a sitting position on the water, they are not as often seen flying above the ocean as are their relatives, the brown pelicans.

These people, the picknickers, surfers, and walking college girls were only a few of the people enjoying the Seashore that day. And every day brings a great variety of people to survey its wonders, to work in its fields or waters, or to explore more deeply its past.

The *estero* has twenty-eight miles of shoreline, most of it at one time or another involved with the history of California. It is easy for a visitor standing on its shores to imagine Drake's ship, *The Golden Hinde,* pulled onto shore, with men busily caulking its seams and mending its sails. Or the visitor might picture the *San Agustin's* crew being welcomed ashore by the Miwok Indians.

Sand has been drifting in from the ocean over the years and the waters of the *estero* are too shallow now for commercial shipping. No schooners ply back and forth across San Francisco Bay any more, but names like Schooner Bay and Creamery Bay remain on maps to remind visitors of the earlier importance of the *estero* for transportation.

Even earlier than the time of the schooners, the Coast Miwok dragged oysters out of the *estero* waters, living off them and the other treasures the ocean waters provided, such as clams, mussels, sturgeon, and sea bass. Today, the *estero* waters still provide food, not only for residents of the San Francisco Bay area, but for people all over the United States. On the largest of the branches of water that form the *estero,* a "water farm" and cannery operates to raise and market choice oysters. The oysters are planted in seed beds in the *estero,* with wooden fences around them to keep crab and stingaree fish—the oyster farmer's chief enemies—from feeding on the young oysters. On a single day a few years ago, the oystermen killed forty-six stingaree fish along the oyster bed fences.

The oyster farm is privately owned, although it operates in waters leased from the state of California and is considered part of the National Seashore. The three men who own the farm, a father and his two sons, are proud of their business and of the methods they have developed to increase oyster production and improve quality. They welcome visitors who want to see their operation.

The Johnson Oyster Farm is reached by a road that turns east from Sir Francis Drake Boulevard, the main road through the Seashore.

Drake's Bay, which includes the *estero,* is of great interest to students of anthropology. Here anthropologists and biologists have found great masses of whale bones set in rocks below the surface of the soil. Some of the bones are around thirty million years old, others no more than thirty, showing the vast span of time that creature life has existed on the peninsula.

To the right of the same main road—a road that ends, eventually, at the Point Reyes Coast Guard Station on the headland—lies the main beach of the Point Reyes peninsula. Called Point Reyes Beach, it gets the full sweep of the Pacific combers along its ten miles of sand and sandstone cliffs. No one swims at Point Reyes Beach because the surf is too rough, but picknickers and beach-combers haunt it winter and summer, in sunshine or fog. Picknickers find fire pits in which to barbecue, and tables and benches placed where the dramatic surf and the sky above it can be watched. Beachcombers find many kinds of driftwood, from massive logs so straight they seem to have been the spars of old sailing ships, to rough boards with metal fittings that once served as hatch covers on ships. Or they pick up small pieces of wood, straight or twisted, with which to build their beach fires. Shells, too, are uncovered by the treasure hunters although the long beach is not one of the best for seashell hunting. In spring, winds blow hundreds of tiny, sail-like, delicate, blue-tinged husks onto the shore. These are the remains of a small sea creature known as "By-the-Wind Sailor", a distant relative of the jellyfish.

Although swimming is prohibited at Point Reyes Beach, surf fishing is popular. Sea bass and perch are among the fish most often caught there.

The park service roads leading to two different portions of the long beach are well-surfaced and open all year. The roads wind through gently rolling meadows that in spring are ornamented by flowering sea figs, brilliantly colored ice plant, sand verbena, and many other plants common to the Pacific Coast. Point Reyes Beach is approximately twenty miles from the National Seashore headquarters.

Another popular beach is only sixteen miles from the park headquarters. This is a small beach and is known as

McClure's, after the family that owned the beach for many years. This beach lies halfway between the headquarters and the tip of Tomales Point and can only be reached by walking a half-mile down a steep trail from the parking area for cars, above the beach. The trail runs between two sides of a deep ravine and overlooks a stream that feeds into the ocean at the edge of the beach. In May, bush lupine, yellow and fragrant, perfumes the air. Orange California poppies mix with the lavender-pink of mariposa lilies and various white-flowered shrubs. Along the stream, shrubs provide hiding places and perches for song sparrows and their relatives, the white-crowns. These birds produce a clear, sweet melody that rises above the distant sound of the ocean below. Near the beach, where the stream spills across the sand toward the ocean, watercress grows thickly but the sand blowing in from the beach would make it difficult to use even if there were no laws against picking plants within the Seashore.

Limantour Spit is a hook of land, mostly sand, that juts into the bay south of Drake's *Estero*. Archaeologists and anthropologists spent months digging into the Indian mounds of the Spit, some of which were half-covered with water. It was in these mounds that pieces of porcelain, later identified as having come from Cermeño's cargo, and long iron spikes, which no Indian of the time could have possessed, were found, establishing with certainty that this was the place where the unfortunate *San Agustín* met disaster. And it is in these mounds, and others in the area, that the life and habits of the Coast Miwok gradually reveals itself to students of anthropology. From the broken bits of shells and from occasional artifacts such as shaped tools for hunting and utensils for cooking, the way of life of these early inhabitants of the peninsula can be told.

On Limantour Spit, also, live some of the most interesting and varied species of animals and birds on the Seashore. Bird banders have found ninety-two different kinds of birds on the Spit. Gray foxes run through the dune grass to hunt for mice and other rodents; a species of mouse known as the Point Reyes jumping mouse lives there and other places on the peninsula. The Spit is also a resting place for sea lions and harbor seals, although the rookery, or breeding ground, for seals is on Double Point, two points of land that jut out from the coast into the bay a little farther south.

Herds of sea lions have been seen and heard in Tomales Bay, the arm of the ocean that divides Point Reyes from the mainland. The bark of the lions can be heard from some distance.

The point of land at the southernmost tip of the Point Reyes peninsula, which gave the Seashore its name, is not legally part of the national park yet. The lighthouse, now over a hundred years old, is open to the public only part of the time, mostly because the Coast Guard Station there does not have facilities to take care of the many visitors who want to visit the headland. The headland is very windy and often very foggy, but despite wind and fog it is a strangely beautiful spot. Below the elevation where the Coast Guard has its buildings, sea lions congregate in great numbers. And on its rocks, murres stand close together in numbers to catch fish in their strong beaks, each female laying its solitary egg on bare rock.

To the North, when the air is clear enough, visitors to the headland can see the long combers of Point Reyes Beach. Out beyond the headlands are the Farallon Islands, a haven for birds, and the site of another Coast Guard Station. To the south is Drake's Bay and in the far distance, Duxbury Reef.

In spring and summer, far below the Coast Guard buildings, the sheer cliffs are draped with the brilliant pink of small-flowered ice plant. Below the plants the current is very swift but schools of fish travel in it on their migrations along the Pacific Coast.

The headquarters of the Point Reyes National Seashore, operated by the National Parks Service, are at the entrance to Bear Valley. A little apart from the administration buildings is a huge red barn. The barn, which is two-thirds the length of a football field, was due to be torn down to make way for a new maintenance equipment building. But a Marin County supervisor, Thomas T. Storer, learned from a specialist in art history that the barn was a superb example of a type of structure that dated back to a time before the birth of Christ. With the help of the Department of the Interior, Storer prevented destruction of the barn. The barn is occupied chiefly by

107

barn owls, bats, sparrows and swallows at present but it may be turned into a museum. The building is on the original land grant give to Rafael Garcia, that early soldier who later became a pioneer settler on the peninsula.

Bear Valley is a major feature of the National Seashore. No cars or motorcycles are permitted on the trails in the Valley, but hikers and horseback riders are welcome. There are a few camping facilities for campers willing to carry their bedrolls and food on their backs.

Trails are well-marked and maps can be obtained at the headquarters. The trails vary in length from three-fourths of a mile, to the long trek through the Valley to the coast, a distance of four and a half miles each way. For more energetic hikers, the Sky Trail goes all the way to the ocean beaches at Bear Valley and is nearly eight miles each way. The Sky Trail goes up the 1407 foot Mount Wittenberg, highest point in the National Seashore. In early spring, a multitude of wildflowers covers the mountain slopes with yellow and blue and pink.

Autumn, too, has color in Bear Valley. Red-barked madrone trees light up the forests of fir and bay and live oak with red-orange clumps of berries. Toyon bushes, sometimes called the Christmas berry bush, provide red of a darker color, and the wild honeysuckle vine winds over and around shrubs to dangle its crimson berries before the hiker's eye.

Probably the most colorful plant in Bear Valley is the poison oak. Its leaves turn a variety of shades of red in autumn, a clear warning to leave this plant alone. A visitor from Europe, unfamiliar with the plant, took a bouquet of the beautiful leaves to her hotel room. Two days later she was in a hospital, her arms, face, and neck full of blisters and swollen painfully.

The Bear Valley trail, despite its length and the poison oak threat, is rewarding. The hiker comes out into a meadow from which he can see masses of rocks standing up in the ocean waters. The rocks were created long before the hiker was born, when the ocean surf cut back the cliffs. These rocks are called stacks, and one of them is a resting place for cormorants. These black birds stand with their long necks erect until they are ready, and then they dive down from the stack into the ocean for food. Pelicans—those same huge brown birds the Indian children watched speed past the beaches hundreds of years ago—also perch on the sea stacks between flights.

Old Pine, the Highland Loop, Meadow Trail, and the short Woodpecker Trail are other trails in the Valley. More trails will be created as funds for development of the Seashore become available. Bear Valley is open all the year around to visitors—there can be rain and fog, but there is never any snow in the Valley.

Other areas to be developed within the Seashore are Abbott's Lagoon, a small lake not far from the coast, where dune picnicking, boating, and fishing will be part of the recreational activities. In time there may be deep sea charter boats, a restaurant, a boat landing and docks on a portion of the Point Reyes headland. Campgrounds will be scattered at suitable locations along the ocean or on the hills above. The rough beginnings of a bird observatory have been established on what was once Palomarin Ranch.

The Point Reyes National Seashore is a place where people who want only to watch the ocean, as well as bird-watchers, abalone hunters, clam diggers, fishermen, camera fans, artists and anyone interested in either sea or land creatures, can pursue their special interests. A twenty-rayed starfish two feet in diameter was found by a biologist on a peninsula beach. Flocks of Brandt geese winter there, and coyotes, bobcats, a rare mountain beaver, make up part of the natural history.

A few, lucky, bright-eyed and patient visitors also enjoy an activity that the Indians must have once enjoyed. During the months from November to late March, the gray whales of the California coast can be seen some distance from shore, on their way south to winter breeding grounds and then back north with their babies to their regular home in the cold waters of the far north. Whale watchers even have a club that each year celebrates the parade of the whales.

One phenomenon not native to the Seashore is the presence of white deer. Some years ago a property owner bought some rare, imported deer from the collection of William Randolph Hearst, Sr. Some of the deer were white, some spotted. The man who bought them turned them loose on Point Reyes; as many as a hundred have been found on one ranch. Sometimes hikers on the Sky Trail see the white deer.

Hundreds of plants are native to the peninsula. Besides the scentless California poppy and the familiar blue, white, and yellow lupine, there are white-edged tidy tips, forget-me-nots turning whole fields to blue, big white cow parsnips, and the pink flower called farewell-to-spring whose seeds were once gathered by the Miwok Indians for food.

Someone has said of the Miwoks that their lives were peaceful and carefree, the kind of life some Americans dream of, especially when they retire from their businesses or professions. Perhaps, for a day or a week or several weeks, people can "retire" for a brief time at the

beautiful peninsula north of San Francisco known as the
Point Reyes National Seashore.

NOTES

THE PENINSULA OF POINT REYES became a national sea-shore because many citizens worked for it. Some of these citizens were young. They acted through organizations such as Camp Fire Girls and Boy and Girl Scouts.

In 1966 a National Conference on Natural Beauty and Conservation was held in Washington, D.C. under the direction of Diana MacArthur, a former Peace Corps worker. Since that first conference, junior citizens have initiated and completed many conservation projects across the country.

In Honolulu, Hawaii, a group of young people fought to keep Diamond Head, an extinct volcano rising over 7,000 feet from the Pacific on the coast of Oahu, from having its slopes marred by developers of high rise apartments.

In Louisiana, eighteen year old Loretta Shadow directed an anti-litter drive under the name CRUD (Campaign to Remove Unsightly Debris). Litter from sixteen miles of Louisiana highways was collected. State officials estimated that CRUD saved the taxpayers over eight thousand dollars and even more importantly, gave their own countryside a cleaner look.

Guidelines for conservation action by young people were worked out by the National Youth Conference. They have been published in a book called *Youth Takes the Lead,* Urban Research Corporation, 5464 South Shore Drive, Chicago, Ill. 60615.

Other publications suggested by conservationists for interested youth are:

ABC'S OF COMMUNITY PLANNING. 1962. 34 pages. Single copy free; 25¢ for each additional copy. Available from the Community Planning Division, Sears, Roebuck and Company, Chicago, Ill. 60607.

ACTION FOR OUTDOOR RECREATION FOR AMERICA. A concise digest of a report of a Presidential commission, with practical suggestions and aids for citizen action. The report places high priority on prompt action to save for public use "the remaining magnificent stretches of unspoiled coastline." 1964. 36 pages. 25¢. Single copies free from The Conservation Foundation, 1250 Connecticut Avenue, Washington, D.C. 20036.

A NATURE CENTER FOR YOUR COMMUNITY. A basic handbook on the values, objectives, elements, and costs of a community nature center and how to go about establishing one. 1962. 40 pages. $1. National Audubon Society, 1130 Fifth Avenue, New York, N.Y. 10028.

AN ENVIRONMENT FIT FOR PEOPLE. Explores "the meaning of conservation"—"the rational use of the environment to achieve the highest quality of living for mankind." The specifics range from air quality and open space in the hearts of our cities to wild lands and the marine environment. "If you want a world fit to live in, you must fight for it now." By Raymond F. Dasmann, an ecologist. 1968. 28 pages. 25¢. Public Affairs Pamphlets, 381 Park Avenue South, New York, N.Y. 10016.

CHALLENGE TO YOUTH. An address by Russell E. Train to the National Youth Conference on National Beauty and Conservation. "Demonstrations that youth cares about environmental contamination will make politicians and and product-makers sit up and take notice." 1966. 12 pages. Free. The Conservation Foundation, 1250 Connecticut Avenue, Washington, D.C. 20036.

CLEAN WATER. A primer on what citizens can do about water pollution. 1968. 48 pages. Free. Izaak Walton League of America, 1326 Waukengan Road, Glenview, Ill. 60025.

COMMUNITY ACTION FOR NATURAL BEAUTY. A no-nonsense guide to effective action on a broad range of local conservation needs. 1968. 36 pages. Single copies free from Citizens Advisory Committee on Recreation and Natural Beauty, 1700 Pennsylvania Avenue, N.W., Washington, D.C. 20006. Also available in quantity at 40¢ from U.S. Government Printing Office, Washington, D.C. 20402.

CONCEPTS OF CONSERVATION. A guide to discussion of some fundamental problems. 1963. 64 pages. Free. The Conservation Foundation, 1250 Connecticut Avenue, Washington, D.C. 20036.

OPEN SPACE ACTION. Study Report 15, by William H. Whyte, 65 cents. Government Printing Office, U.S.A.

SIGNS OUT OF CONTROL. California Roadside Council, 12 Garces Drive, San Francisco, 94132. 75 cents.